O9-ABE-644

Technological & Socioeconomic Development: A Third World Challenge

Dr. Anthony I. Akubue, Professor
Environmental and Technological Studies
St. Cloud State University
St. Cloud, Minnesota 56301

Copyright © 2012 Anthony I.Akubue

All rights reserved. No part of this book may be reproduced in any form or by any electronic or mechanical means including information storage and retrieval systems without permission in writing from the author except where permission is noted within the book for personal use or except by a reviewer who may quote brief passages in a review.

SecondPrinting

Sunray Publishing

21253 22nd Ave. S

St. Cloud, MN 56301

www.yourbookpublisher.net

Manufactured in the United States of America   ISBN: 0-9785081-0-6

Distributed by:
Nwakibie Distributions
1720 10th Ave. S.
St. Cloud, MN 56304

Preface

Third World development is an area that has commanded intense research interest since the end of World War II. Much has been written about the Third World and its development challenges. I started thinking of writing this book after some years of searching in vain for a textbook that would address the focus of an undergraduate course I teach at St. Cloud State University. Many of the books I reviewed had a few chapters that were relevant but nothing more. I was looking for a book for the uninitiated that explained the challenges of Third World development in simple every day terms, without much professional jargon. I was looking for a book that addressed the realities of the Third World with less rhetoric and political ideology. In my frustration I began to consider the idea of writing a book myself. This idea became reality when Technological and Socioeconomic Development: A Third World Challenge materialized.

The purpose of this book is to challenge university undergraduate students to seek to understand what matters in the study of Third World development. Most people today see scientific and technological progress as the basis for general progress. The idea is that poverty, unemployment, inequality, malnutrition, and other social problems will improve with advances in science-based technologies. The assumption is that technological progress automatically produces socioeconomic progress. It is true that technology is an important agent of change, but it is only a means to an end. Technology is not valued for its own sake, but in the expectation that it will lead to better conditions of life for the masses. Over 50 years of technology transfer to the Third World have not translated into improved well being for the majority of people in the region.

The fact is that development concerns people and their ability to help themselves. Development entails growth and change; that is, positive change leading to poverty reduction, decreasing unemployment, reducing inequality, and increasing access to basic needs for increasing number of people. Growth has to be accompanied by distribution; because growth does not assist the poor if it does not reach the poor.

i

Years of expectation that growth will trickle down to the poor in the long run have met with disappointment. Development is about reducing Third World dependence on the West, about Third World self-reliance, and increasing the capability of Third World countries to take charge of their own development. When authentic development is taking place, human resources are being enhanced through improving knowledge, education for the masses, technical training to provide skills for the workforce, and the development of an entrepreneurial class who leads a country in innovations. For this to happen, development experts must realize that Third World countries are so different from each other that development strategies must not be based on a "one size fits all" mentality.

The fact is that the Third World is not only made up of countries with great internal diversity, they are also at different points on the development continuum. Since the countries have different conditions, problems, needs, traditions, and culture, development strategies must be tailored to address the uniqueness of each country.

The book consists of seven chapters, starting with chapter one on identifying the Third World. This chapter traces the origin of the name Third World, the original spirit associated with the term, and changes that have taken place in its interpretation. Chapter two discusses the characteristics associated with the Third World. Chapter three discusses development and ways it might be approached if it is to lead the Third World self-reliance and self-sufficiency. Chapter four discusses the basic needs strategy and the human development approach intended to complement the conventional development strategy based on growth. Chapter five deals with technology and technology transfer to the Third World. It stresses understanding the meaning of technology as a prerequisite to understanding technology transfer and why it is not helping the Third World very much. Chapter six addresses the issue of appropriate technology and the need to widen the technological options available to the Third World. Finally, chapter seven deals with gender issues relative to Third World technological and socioeconomic development. It calls attention to the lack of access to vital resources for women and what should be done.

Dedication

To Jesus Christ, the image of the invisible God, for loving and taking cares of me. To my parents, Jerome and Grace Akubue, who taught me to worship and live in the fear of God. To my children—Anthony I. Akubue, Jr., Jerome C. Akubue II, and Grace N. Akubue II—my precious gifts from God. And to Georgina N. Akubue, my deceased wife and the mother of my children, for the love and pleasant memories we shared.

Contents

Chapter Five
Technology and Technology Transfer
for Third World Development   87

Chapter Six
Appropriate Technology:
Widening the Technological
Options for Third World
Development   115

Chapter Seven
Technology, Development,
and Gender Disparity   145

Chapter ONE
Identifying the Third World

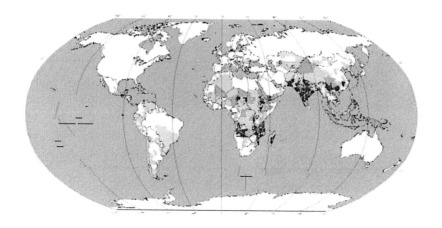

Where is the "Third World"?

      First of all, long before the phrase *Third World* became popular and gained widespread usage, different attempts had been made to introduce a countervailing force to ease the rivalry a source of global polarization and tension between two opposing and competing political ideologies. I will say more on this shortly. In the mean time, there is an on-going debate on what constitutes the Third World and whether the term is still relevant given the collapse of the Soviet Union and communist bloc formerly known as the Second World. I will address the latter in another section of the chapter. Meanwhile, a review of the literature reveals a growing consensus on the regions and countries that constitute the Third World. The continents of Africa, Asia, and Latin America are commonly identified as the locus of Third World countries. In his book, Dorraj (1995) described the *Third World* as "the developing countries of Asia,

1

Latin America, Africa, and the Middle East" (p. 3). Wolf (1988) was more elaborate when he identified the Third World as the entire

world outside Europe, Anglo-America, Anglo-Oceania, Japan and the Soviet Union. (Anglo-America is the United States and Canada; Anglo-Oceania consists of Australia and New Zealand.) Although South Africa is sometimes excluded, the historical, cultural, and economic conditions of the overwhelming majority of its population warrant inclusion. Israel is included on the basis of its location and the origin of the majority of its people, while Portugal and the Balkans are excluded on the same basis, though in terms of purely economic criteria, such as their gross national product (GNP), they could qualify for inclusion. (p. 99)

In this book, the countries of the world collectively referred to as the Third World in Africa, Asia (except Japan and the former Soviet Union), Latin America (Mexico, Central and South America), the Caribbean, the Middle East, and Oceania (minus Australia and New Zealand) make up three quarters of humanity. In a world the United Nations has projected would have 7 billion people by October 31, 2011 (Madsen, 2011), that would be about 5.25 billion people occupying two-thirds of the surface of planet Earth. This Third World is made up of more than one hundred politically independent nations, including the newly independent Republic of South Sudan, whose political independence from former Sudan came to fruition in on July, 2011, becoming the 193rd member of United Nation on July 14, 2011.

As will be shown later, most of these countries, with the exception of Latin American countries, have a recent history of colonial rule and political independence. The main purpose of this chapter is to explore the etymology of the phrase *Third World*; that is, tracing the history of the phrase, when it was coined and why, and the original and prevailing usage of the term.

The Geopolitical *Third World*

Although the phrase *Third World* is of a recent coinage, it is also seen as the outcome of attempts long before the French introduced it to find a third alternative capable of ameliorating an age-old rivalry between two opposing political ideologies of communism and capitalism. This rivalry was so acrimonious and hostile it was creating global polarization and much political tension. Back in Europe in the 1920s, the possibility of a *third way* was seriously discussed as a political arena that was "neither explicitly capitalist nor explicitly socialist in orientation" (Toye, 1987, p. 6). It was an idea that the rivalry between communism and capitalism could be better handled and did not have to be overwhelming and destabilizing. Again, in 1947, a British Labor Party pamphlet known as *Keep Left*, possibly the precursor of today's *left* and *right* political labels, carried a message that favored the introduction of a *Third Force* in world affairs, for the sake of preventing the antagonizing and polarizing relationship of the capitalist West and the socialist East (Fieldhouse, 1999). This, too, was intended as a mitigating or tension-diffusing force. The name *Third World* emerged soon after in the second decade after World War II. It was an invention of a more recent, intense, and pervasive Cold War era, a time characterized by fierce ideological bipolarity and incredible political tension. It was a world of two superpowers and their associated blocs of influence. It was the Western bloc of capitalist ideology, led by the United States, and the Eastern bloc of communist ideology, led by the Soviet Union. As Waites (1999) described it, "The USA and the Soviet Union could plausibly represent themselves as leading two 'worlds,' with different social and political systems and ideologies, whose antagonism was so pervasive as to exclude all possibility of neutrality" (p. xiii).

The period was also characterized by indigenous movements for independence and self-determination among European colonies in Africa and Asia. Under great and persistent pressure from native nationalists, the European colonizers realized that so long as this pressure continued unabated they would have to do that which was inevitable: grant political independence to the colonies. Such was the situation when the concept of a *Third World* was introduced.

Of European origin, the term emerged in the early 1950s from the work of French authors. The French demographer and economist Alfred Sauvy is especially credited with using the phrase for the first time in his article that appeared in a French magazine, *L'Observateur*, on August 14, 1952 (Sauvy, 1970; Mason, 1997). Sauvy (1952) observed that the Third World (*tiers monde*) was like the Third Estate (*tiers estat*) of France before the French Revolution of 1789, and like the Third Estate, 'This Third World, ignored, exploited, scorned, wishes to stand up for itself' (Sauvy, 1952). The Third World wanted to be free of colonialism, imperialism, and other forms of foreign domination; it wanted independence and self-determination.

The Third Estate, a group of peasants, workers in the cities, and the middle class consisting of prosperous merchants, lawyers, and government officials, was considered subordinate to the privileged First Estate or the clergy, and Second Estate or the nobility. Dissatisfied with its subordination and treatment, the Third Estate took advantage of a rare opportunity made possible by a quarrel between the nobility and clergy to confront the privileged estates in the French Revolution of 1789. When the dust finally settled, France was politically, socially, and economically transformed into a society of equal citizenship. Ironically, the conflict between the United States and the Soviet Union provided a similar political opportunity that led to independence for Third World countries in Africa and Asia.

Why "Third World"?

By naming them the *Third World,* Alfred Sauvy alluded to the potential for a revolution that was fomenting in the colonies as they aspired toward independence and self-determination. Not only did Sauvy write that the Third World had a destiny of revolution just like the Third Estate of France, but that the term also suggested non-alignment with either United States-led capitalist world or Soviet

Union-led Socialist world. *Third World,* as originally conceived, was a forward-looking and hopeful way of describing what was happening at the time in Africa and Asia. It was a phrase purposely meant to describe the people of that world mainly from their own perspective, and not from a Western perspective, as we generally seem to do today (Grimm, 1990). In fact, Sedghi (1994) made the point implicitly when she described the Third World as "societies whose contemporary histories include resistance to colonialism, national liberation movements and revolutions, and survival in the age of the internationalization of capital and labor" (p. 92). Admittedly, the term does carry the connotation of superiority and might be considered somewhat patronizing with its French origin. However, Vale (1998) noted that the sense in which the French used the term was different from how it is used today. Vale (1998) claimed "the *third* of *Third World* is from the French for *third* as a fraction rather than *third* as in position, place or order" (p. 2). Also writing on this subject, Rossi (1963) observed:

> *The Third World took a place after World War II, alongside the Western World and the Communist World. It is Third not only because the other two preceded it, dominating the scene of history, but also insofar as it possesses a personality of its own, just as the others do. It is not a world waiting to choose which side to join because it has already chosen to be itself. Its vision of the future, its needs, its perspective are different, and these are all incompatible with the idea that the world can be either democratic in the Western sense or socialist in the Soviet sense. To the old alternative it has added one of its own. (p. 4)*

The revolutionary potential that Sauvy foresaw began when nationalist movements for the independence of the colonies sprouted at different places, ushering in a revolutionary epoch in the years that followed. Rossi (1963) could not have stated this development any better when he wrote that "the European powers abandoned one territory after another not because they lacked the strength to hold them, but because they recognized the relentlessness of the revolutionary process" (p. 19).

5

The Third World: The Outcome of Western Guilt and Politics?

Not everyone believed in the story of the Third World told thus far. There were those who argued that the Third World was not the result of history, geography, or economics. Essentially this position downplayed or ignored the reality of superpower rivalry. The Third World, according to this argument, was created and the creative force was a combination of psychology and politics. This view holds that the Third World was the product of the guilt felt in the West for its acts of exploitation in the past as well as the politics of foreign aid. Bauer (1972) disagreed that the West was responsible for the poverty of the Third World, and claimed in a rather weak argument that "while it is not true colonialism brought about poverty, there is some truth in the notion that poverty brought colonialism" (pp. 150-151). Arguing that the guilt assumed by the West was unwarranted, Bauer (1972) opined that the notion of Western-induced poverty in the Third World, though unfounded, was effectively promoted by powerful and influential groups or individuals with vested interests mainly in the West. It was, therefore, this successful implantation of this feeling of guilt in the West that was responsible for unleashing a regime of foreign aid to the Third World. Despite profuse historical evidence to the contrary, Bauer (1981) concluded not with intellectually persuasive arguments but with hollow ethnocentric statements that foreign aid was responsible for creating the Third World and that without foreign aid there would be no Third World. One can only take this apparent distortion of history with a grain of salt. Writing and saying the same thing everywhere possible neither makes it true nor impart sense into what is immediately demonstrable as nonsense.

This same school of thought believed that the Third World was hostile to the West because of its alleged political leaning in favor of socialism. However, this allegation is weak since the socialist world also denounced the Third World for allegedly being subordinated to the capitalist world of the West. This then is an argument in which the "second world (socialism) will not recognize the third, on the pretext that the third is really part of the first. But the first will not do so either, on the pretext that the third is indistinguishable from the second" (Toye, 1983, p. 7).

The Non-Aligned Movement (NAM)

In any case the popularity of the *Third World* concept in the 1960s was accompanied by the formation of numerous independence movements in the Third World. One of the early major movements to emerge was the Non-Aligned Movement (NAM). The notion of non-alignment surfaced in the process of decolonization and formation, as attention was turned toward correcting the ruins of former colonial empires at the same time as many of the colonies were becoming independent states. Just before India's independence in 1947, Jawaharlal Nehru the country's first Prime Minister was credited with writing emphasizing that India would favor "a policy of its own as a free state, not as a satellite of another nation" (Orlov, 2002, p. 50). Different conferences preceded the formation of the

Sidang Kemuncak
Negara-Negara Berkecuali Ke XIII
XIII Conference of Heads of State or Government
of The Non-Aligned Movement

XIII Conference of NAM

Non-aligned Movement. One of these held in New Delhi in March 1947, shortly before India's independence, was aimed at ensuring amity between Asian countries. Prominent among the outcomes of this gathering was the collective wish of the countries not to participate in military blocs and alliances (Orlov, 2002). However, the conference that involved much of the planning for the eventual emergence of the Non-aligned Movement was that attended by delegates from 29 Asian and African countries at Bandung, Indonesia, from April 17 through 24, 1955 (Mason, 1997; Gonzalez, 1998). As the beginning of the political emergence of the Third World, the Bandung conference owed its organization partly to the major role played by China and India, as they campaigned vigorously for its inception. It was at this conference that the term *Third World* was used for the first time by the people whom Alfred Sauvy had given the name. The Bandung conference played some very important roles. First, it brought together African and Asian leaders after they had been insulated from each other's influence as colonies. The conference therefore provided a vital opportunity for the new leaders to get acquainted and discuss problems of common interest. It was also a get-together that demonstrated the diverse nature of the countries representing the Third World (Rossi, 1963). The conference adopted, among other things, five principles known as *Panch Shila*, namely, respect for territorial integrity and sovereignty, nonaggression, noninterference in domestic affairs, equality and mutual benefits, peaceful coexistence and economic cooperation (Rossi, 1963).

The NAM was established officially at its first Non-Aligned summit conference of heads of state and government in Belgrade, Yugoslavia, in 1961, with representatives from 25 countries in attendance (Gonzalez, 1998). Its purpose, as declared in the Havana Declaration of 1979, is to preserve "the national independence, sovereignty, territorial integrity and security of non-aligned countries " in their "struggle against imperialism, colonialism, neocolonialism, apartheid, racism, including Zionism, and all forms of foreign aggression, occupation, domination, interference or hegemony as well as against great power and bloc politics." Indian Prime Minister Jawaharlal Nehru, one of the founding fathers of the NAM, used the term *non-alignment* for the first time as a political term in an April 1954 speech in Colombo Sri Lanka. Vickers (1999) wrote that "Nehru envisioned the idea of non-alignment not as passive neutrality, but as a policy of vigorous action for peace and for better international climate" (p. 2). As Nehru himself remarked, the word "nonaligned has a negative meaning, but if you give it a positive connotation it means nations which object to this lining-up for war purposes military blocs, military alliances and the like. Therefore we keep away from this and we want to throw our weight, such as it is, in favor of peace (Rossi, 1963, p.95). Non-alignment meant that these countries eschewed commitment to either the capitalist ideology of the First World or that of the communist Second World, hence constituting a

Third World. As Merriam (1988) put it, the Third World became a positive concept symbolizing the new and experimental arena of global politics of neither capitalist nor communist ideology. This is not to say that all of these new countries remained neutral and did not take sides with either the Soviet Union or the United States at the time. Individual countries had bilateral relationships with the superpower they desired. At the same time, the countries were aware that sympathizing with one superpower ideology or the other would jeopardize or detract from their goal of Third World viability and undermine the decolonization process. By implication, nonalignment "means that a country committed to it will not identify itself with a military bloc as a matter of policy, but will decide each problem on its on merits; this is not the same as isolation or neutralism or indifference" (Rossi, 1963, p. 93). Julius Nyerere, the first Prime Minister of independent Tanganyika (now Tanzania), explained the position of the Third World thus:

> *We give notice now that no one will be able to count on an automatic vote from simply because we are their friends. Nor should any country which feels unfriendly toward us assume that we shall automatically vote on the opposite side to it. We shall not automatically condemn a policy because it is said to be a communist plot. Nor shall we necessarily oppose a policy because it is described by its opponents as an imperialist intrigue. We shall look at every issue in the light of whether we believe it supports the cause of freedom, of justice, and of peace in the world. (Rossi, 1963, p. 93)*

Not only was nonalignment an anti-colonialism movement, it was also intended to serve as a mechanism for peace and détente between the two superpowers. Of special interest to the NAM was the peaceful co-existence of the two superpowers. It was important to Third World countries to induce the two superpowers to reconcile their differences. To do this, the unaligned must show impartiality, even when no superpower is likely to consider a country impartial that does not take its side (Rossi, 1963). Having the two competing powers renounce the idea of victory, and getting them to accept the principle of peaceful coexistence as understood by the Third World was of paramount importance to the nonaligned. Of course the NAM also took the stand to avoid condemning either of the superpowers as this would not facilitate influencing them to maintain peace. To the nonaligned, therefore, taking sides as a group was anathema.

The creation of the NAM provided a vitally needed forum for the Third World to articulate its views, propose solutions to common problems, and maintain a united front against pressures and actions by the competing superpowers (Manley, 1990). In his eloquent speech at the 8th summit conference of the NAM in Harare, Zimbabwe, the late Prime Minister Rajiv Gandhi of India reminded his colleagues of the raison deter of the Non-Aligned Movement.

> *Our movement arose out of our fight against foreign rule, imperialism and colonialism. Its purpose is to give body and shape to our vision of freedom and equality. We adhere to non-alignment because non-alignment symbolizes the courage to be ourselves, because it proclaims our faith in a new kind of world a world of equals and because it is a compact with peace. The world can survive only by giving up confrontation and by eradicating fear, hate and disparity. This is the thrust of our movement. (pp. 37-38)*

At its 1973 summit conference in Algiers, Algeria, the NAM expanded its strategic areas of interest to include global economic as well as political issues. This was in recognition that it must work not in isolation but collaboratively with organizations with similar interests. A good case in point was the NAM collaboration with the Group of 77 (G-77) Third World countries to press for a New International Economic Order (NIEO) at the Sixth Special Session of the UN General Assembly in May 1974 (Vickers, 1999). More will be said on the NIEO concept in the chapter on development. Meanwhile, I will take a moment for a brief discussion of the G-77.

The Group of 77

The G-77 is another major nationalist movement that was founded during the Cold War era. It was formed at the end of the first session of the United Nations Conference on Trade and Development (UNCTAD) in Geneva, Switzerland, on June 15, 1964 (G-77, 1998; Melkote and Merriam, 1998). Established by the joint action of 77 countries, the G-77 is the largest Third World coalition in the United Nations with a membership of about 136 countries. The role of the G-77 is to articulate and promote the joint economic interests of its membership, enhance the group's joint negotiating capacity on all major international economic issues in the United Nations system, and promote economic and technical cooperation among the member countries (G-77, 1998). The group's priorities, as stated by K. D. Knight, the Jamaican Minister of foreign affairs and foreign trade, are: increasing the flow of resources to developing countries; improvements in global governance; formulation of a development agenda; enhancing South/South co-operation,; and disaster management and relief (Knight, 2005, pp. 2-3). As indicated above, the G-77 has about 136 member countries but maintains its current name because of its historical and psychological significance.

Geopolitical to Social and Economic Emphasis

Today, the most widely emphasized interpretation of the *Third World* associates it with social and economic backwardness. The *Third World* still means countries, but refers to conditions as well, especially conditions of destitution and disorder (Mason, 1997). Lane (1992) blamed this development on intellectuals and politicians, whom she claimed, added a socio-economic connotation to its original geopolitical meaning. Going by this interpretation, the *third* in *Third World* has come to symbolize position or order, and depicts Third World countries as *third rate* or *third class*. For moralists such as Zachariah (1992), this connotation has been attached to the phrase just to dehumanize nonwhite people and to ignore the actual context of their existence. Naipaul (1985) described the phrase *Third World* as a bloodless universality that robs individuals and societies of their particularities. Whatever differences there may be between countries, and there are quite many, are by this interpretation swept under the rug and ignored. The mere mention of the *Third World* now conjures up images of socially and economically impoverished countries. *Third World* now symbolizes countries that are perennially dependent upon the industrialized countries of Europe, North America, and Japan for survival. As far as most people are concerned, Third World countries are similar socially and economically, and possess a set of common characteristics. Merriam (1988), described the Third World as countries in Asia, Africa, and Latin America, "which generally are characterized by relatively low per capita income, high rates of illiteracy, agricultural economies, short life expectancies, low degrees of social mobility, strong attachments to tradition and, usually, a history of colonization" (p.15). Alfred Sauvy was apparently persuaded to do what was in vogue when he opted to emphasize the social and economic dimension of the *Third World* different from his initial political emphasis. Sauvy (1970) wrote that Third World countries were countries with "a high birth rate, above 4 percent; a rapid growth of population of the order of 2 to 3.5 percent a year; a small national income per inhabitant, of the order of $100 − 350 a year; and a mainly agricultural economy" (p. 204). Of course these characteristics are relative as Corbridge (1988) observed: "Quite explicitly, the 'Third World' was measured against the First World and as a bloc found wanting" (p. 45).

Unfortunately one of the dangers of generalizing about Third World countries in this manner is that it tends to obscure the individual realities of these nations. Third World countries have more factors setting them apart than those they have in common. In reality, Third World countries are sharply differentiated, for they include countries on various levels of social and economic development. Rieff (1989) observed that Third World countries have:

> *little or nothing in common with one another in terms of their economic systems, their political arrangements, or, for that matter, the destinies*

that one can begin to predict for their peoples. As political or economic shorthand, the term 'Third World' is all but valueless. The planet has become far too plural a place for anyone but the most naïve or sentimental person to believe that all these brown and yellow people live under the same arrangements or are motivated by the same creeds. The Third World is not a concept that can be applied to the long continuum of history. (p. 63)

One of the few attributes that Third World countries seem to share in common is that most of them are the beneficiaries of foreign aid from the industrialized nations. This foreign aid regime was initiated only during the Cold War era as the two superpowers sought to attract allies in a bipolar world of capitalism and communism. Lord Peter Bauer (1988) argued that apart from foreign aid, Malaysia and Mozambique, Nepal and Argentina, India and Chad, Tuvalu and Brazil, Burma (Myanmar) and Nigeria could not possibly have much else in common between them. Bauer (1988) wrote:

The people of Asia, Africa, and Latin America live in the most diverse physical, cultural, social and political environments. They differ in many respects—in cultural, technical, and commercial sophistication, in political arrangements, and in income, wealth, and economic progress. They were not aggregated into a single category of supposedly common characteristics and interests until the beginning of aid…. It is condescending for people in the West to regard them as being a largely undifferentiated and stagnant mass. (p. 66)

Arguments such as these, coupled with the collapse of the Soviet bloc, the end of the Cold War, the economic transformation of former Soviet satellite economies and their growing participation in global markets have raised questions about the relevance of the *Third world* label and the need for the continued existence of groups such as the NAM. Arguing similarly, Zoellick (2010) remarked that "if 1989 saw the end of the 'Second World' with Communism's demise, then 2009 saw the end of what was known as the 'Third World.'" The demise of the Third World in this case is linked with the development of a multi-polar global economy in which a number of Third World countries have experienced unprecedented growth and considered emerging economic powers. However, the Non-aligned Movement and similar groups have argued that their continued existence is inevitable as a result of neocolonialism, indirect forms of interference, which continue to pose a threat to Third World economic and technological viability. One can understand the persistence and apprehension among ~~of~~ these organizations particularly with the current Western financed and interest in globalization. While Western Europe expansion created colonies and carried out colonialism, the entire West i.e., Western Europe and North America is the purveyor of systemic neocolonialism in the Third World today.

Regarding the relevance of the *Third World* label, Naipaul (1985) argued that the existence of a *Third World* can be no more than mythical in view of the great internal diversity of the countries in question. So intense was his disdain for the label that Naipaul (1988) described it as "a flabby Western concept lacking the flesh and blood of the actual" (p. 10). Colburn (2006) dismissed the label as not only misleading in today's realities, but a concept that is dated and no longer conceptually useful.

There are, however, those who have argued for its retention (Merriam, 1988; Samuelson, 1990). They contend that *Third World* is by far better than "primitive," uncivilized," "barbaric," "backward," "underdeveloped," "undeveloped," and "less developed countries," these countries and their peoples are also called. They have also been called developing and the south. To call them developing countries is to imply that there are countries that are no longer developing, which is not true. Calling them the south because a majority of the countries are located south of the equator ignores the fact that some industrialized countries are also located there. They have also been called low income countries. Again, while many of them are low income countries, it is no secret that some of the countries have incomes higher than some industrialized countries. So, writing in favor of retaining the Third World name, Merriam (1988) argued that "no other phrase seems to achieve greater clarity and simplicity" (p. 20). Adding his own opinion on the issue, Samuelson (1990) concluded that "the label may linger until someone invents a new one to describe today's more muddled situation. The *Third World* still sounds nice; it just doesn't mean much" (p. 45).

Concluding Remarks

From the preceding account, it is apparent that the concept of the *Third World* has undergone some changes in meaning over the years. What started out as a prediction of things to come: of freedom and independence for former colonies, took on a negative and, some times, derogatory meaning. The perversion of the phrase, the end of the Cold War epoch, and the fall of the Soviet bloc collectively set in motion a concerted attack on the relevance of the term and the campaign to discontinue its use. It must be acknowledged, however, that communism is still around and genuine peace continues to be elusive in the world. Judging from the original meaning, *Third World* seems quite benign and preferable to many current alternatives. Moreover, many citizens of the Third World seem to be at ease with the phrase and do not appear insulted by or resentful of the name. In spite of its vagueness and controversy, the term continues to enjoy high ratings on the preference scale. Only time will tell if the objections of its critics will prove strong enough to drive the phrase into extinction.

References

Bauer, P. T. (1972). Dissent on development: Studies and debates in development economics. Cambridge, MA: Harvard University Press.

Bauer, P. T. (1981). Equality, the Third World and economic delusion. Cambridge, MA: Harvard University Press.

Bauer, P. (1988, April). Creating the Third World: Foreign aid and its offspring. Encounter, 80 (4), 66 – 75.

Colburn, F. D. (2006, Spring). Good-bye to the Third World. DISSENT, pp. 38-43

Corbridge, S. (1988). The Third World in global context. In Pacione, M. (Ed.), The geography of the Third World: progress and prospect, pp. 31-76. NY: Routledge.

Dorraj, M. (1995). Introduction: The changing context of Third World political economy. Boulder, CO: Lynne Rienner Publishers, Inc.

Fieldhouse, D. K. (1999). The West and the Third World: Trade, colonialism, dependence, and development. Malden, MA: Blackwell Publishers, Inc.

Gandhi, R. (1987, March-April). An overview of non-alignment. The Black Scholar, 37 – 39.

Grimm, W. J. (1990, May). The 'Third' World. America, 162 (17), 449 – 451.

Group of 77, (1998). The Group of 77. http://www.g77.org/geninfo/whatis77.htm.

Knight, K. D. (2005). A speech at the handing over ceremony of the chairmanship of the Group of 77 in New York, on January 25, 2005. http://www.g77.org/Speeches/0125b.htm

Lane, C. (1992, April 27). Let's abolish the Third World. Newsweek, p. 43.

Madsen, E. L. (2011, May). World population projected to hit 7 billion on October 31. Grist Magazine, Inc. Retrieved from http://www.grist.org/population/2011-05-03-world-population-projected-to-hit-7-billion-o...

Manley, M. (1990, Fall). Southern needs. Foreign Policy, 80, 40 – 51.

Mason, M. (1997). Development and disorder. Hanover, NH: University Press of New England.

Melkote, S. R. and Merriam, A. H. (1998). The Third World: Definitions and new perspectives on development. In A. Gonzalez and J. Norwine (Eds.), The new Third World (pp. 9 – 27). (2nd ed.). Boulder, CO: Westview Press.

Merriam, A. H. (1988). What does "Third World" mean? In J. Norwine and A. Gonzalez (Eds.), The Third World: States of mind and being (pp. 99 – 111). London, England: Unwin Hyman, Ltd.

Naipaul, S. (1985, May 18). A thousand million invisible men. The Spectator, 9 – 11.

Orlov, A. (2002). The Non-Aligned Movement: 40 years after. International Affairs, pp. 49-56

Rieff, D. (1989, Winter). In the Third World. Sal Magundi, 80, 61 – 65.

Rossi, M. (1963). The Third World: The unaligned countries and the world revolution. New York: Funk & Wagnallis.

Samuelson, R. J. (1990, July). End of the Third World. Newsweek, 116 (4), 45.

Sauvy, A. (1952, August 15). Trois mondes, une planete. L'Observateur

Sauvy, A. (1970). General Theory of population. New York, NY: Basic Books, Inc.

Sorenson, G., Poku, N., & Pettiford, L. (1998). Introduction: Redefining the Third World. In N. Poku, L. Pettiford (Eds.), Redefining the Third World (pp. 1 – 15). New York, NY: St. Martin's Press.

Sedghi, H. (1994). Third World feminist perspectives on world politics. In P. R. Beckman and F. D'Amico (Eds.), Women, gender, and world politics: Perspectives, policies, and prospects (89 – 105). Westport, CT: Bergin and Garvey.

Toye, J. (1987). Dilemmas of development: Reflections on the counter-revolution in development theory and policy. New York: Basil Blackwell Inc.

Vickers, B. (1999). Political history of Non-Aligned Movement. [On-line] Available: http://www.igd.org.za/nam/nam_documents/history.html

Waites, B. (1999). Europe and the Third World: From colonization to decolonizationc. 1500-1998.New York: St. Martin's Press.

Wolf, L. G. (1988). The poorest of us all. In J. Norwine and A. Gonzalez (Eds.), The Third World: States of mind and being (pp. 99 – 111). London, England: Unwin Hyman, Ltd.

Zachariah, M. (1992, November). Letter to the editor. (Response to literacy assessment in the Third World) Comparative Education Review, 36 (4), 551 – 554.

Zoellick, R. B. (2010, Spring). The end of the Third World: The case for modernizing multilateralism. The international Economy, pp. 40-43.

Chapter Two

Characteristics of Third World Countries

Introduction

Compared with the technologically advanced countries assuming they mirror the standards to emulate the social, economic, political, educational, and technological accomplishments of Third World nation are limited. This fact is invariably depicted in the characteristics now used to define the Third World as synonymous with conditions of social and economic backwardness. Third World countries are characterized by low literacy rates, as agricultural economies, as having low quality human capital, as countries that are mired in the vicious cycle of poverty, as an overpopulated region, etc. It is on the basis of this comparison that the characteristics below are identified and discussed. As the reader goes over the characteristics, it is quite necessary to keep in mind that growth and socioeconomic changes have been taking place in many Third World countries, resulting in remarkable social and economic transformation. Viewed holistically, the achievements in human development attained in Third World countries in three decades have been unprecedented. The per capita gross national product of Third World economies has nearly doubled over the last generation. Summers (1992) observed that during this period the Third World grew faster than the United Kingdom during the Industrial Revolution, faster than the United States in the period of rapid growth as it came to economic maturity, and faster than Japan during its prewar growth spurt. It is generally the case that discussions of these characteristics often avoid accounting for the circumstances that gave rise to prevailing

Third World conditions. Where attempts are made to explain what led to unenviable condition they are often misleading due mostly to biases associated with ethnocentrism. For example, one reality that receives little or no publicity is the fact that the so-called population problem in the developing world is a relatively recent phenomenon that came with emerging progress in the region. Access to better medicine, healthcare facilities and basic needs, reduced infant mortality rates, and increasing life span, all came with improving socioeconomic conditions in the Third World. This in turn resulted in greater number of children surviving to adulthood and more people living longer. Before the 20th century, high birth rates were matched with high mortality rates, but industrialization and general progress in the 20th century led to declining mortality rates without a matching reduction in birth rates. The inevitable result has been a burgeoning population in the Third World.

The purpose of this chapter is primarily to identify and discuss some of the characteristics that are generally associated with the Third World. The chapter will also show that the Third World does experience progressive socioeconomic changes, and, contrary to popular belief, no single reason can explain away the cause of any prevailing conditions in the region.   What follows, then, is a discussion of some of the characteristics often used in relation to Third World countries.

Colonial Heritage and Political Independence

The areas that are collectively known as the Third World Africa, Asia (except Japan and the Commonwealth of Independent States), Latin America, Oceania (except Australia and New Zealand), and the Middle East are characterized by recent history of colonial rule and political independence. The new countries were colonized by various European nations for periods varying from a few decades (Syria, Lebanon, Iraq, etc.) to five centuries (Mozambique, Jamaica, etc.). The countries in Latin America that obtained their independence earlier than those in Africa and Asia have remained under the political hegemony of Europe and North America directed from London, Paris, New York, and Berlin. For many of these new countries, especially in Africa and Asia, political independence came in the post-World War II period, a time of great super power rivalry known as the Cold War era. As neophyte nation-states, most of the countries are learning by trial and error and continue to struggle with policy formulation, implementation, and self-governance. Worthy of mention, however, is that gaining political independence without economic independence is to a significant degree a guarantee that most of these new countries will remain dependent on the West and Japan.

Traditional Societies

Gemeinschaft is a sociological designation for or a description of close-knit communities, often found in rural areas, where strong personal bonds unite members (Schaefer & Lamm, 1989). Sociologist Ferdinand Tonnies in 1887 used the term to describe the traditional communal life in Germany that was characterized by group solidarity. This traditional lifestyle was giving way to Gesellschaft, the impersonal and individualistic behavior commonly found in urban areas. Third World societies, the rural areas in particular, are described as where communal life remains evident; the individual is secondary to the community, and group solidarity is much valued over individualism. Things are much different in industrialized societies where the social structure has become more complex; relationships between people have become more impersonal, transient, and fragmented. Merriam (1988) noted that in some ways the cultures of the Third World are rich psychologically and spiritually, because they still retain the contentment and sense of tradition sorely lacking in hectic, life-in-a-fast-lane, depersonalized industrial societies. Some of the consequences of this lifestyle are very high divorce and suicide rates in many industrialized countries. Unfortunately, advances in transportation and communication technologies are ushering in an era of monoculture world-wide. This lifestyle, once limited to industrialized societies, is becoming evident in many countries of the Third World where it is beginning to have the same effects.

However, the modernization theorists have a different interpretation for the way things are in the Third World. According to the modernization theory, traditional societies are backward in social and economic sense because they maintain certain beliefs that are not congenial to material progress. This theory posits that traditional societies in the Third World believe in superstition, fatalism, tribalism, maintain rigid social structures, agrarian and rural lifestyle, and suffer from venality and ineptitude, all of which constitute an obstacle to progress. Bauer (1981), a modernist, predictably attributed lack of progress in the Third World to the prevalence of political, social, and personal factors and policies of many governments, which he claimed were not conducive to national advancement. He wrote that in the Third World "people often refuse to abandon attitudes and mores which obstruct economic performance; they are not prepared to give up their established ways for the sake of greater prosperity" (p. 71). It is not totally surprising that most modernists, many of whom are Europeans and North Americans, like to peddle the idea that the Third World is solely to blame for its own lack of prosperity. This, it seems, is a deliberate attempt to disseminate misinformation that Europe had no complicity in the incapacitation and impoverishment of the Third World during and after the colonial era. Economist Peter Thomas Bauer, a Hungarian-born immigrant in England, was conferred the title of "Lord" in 1983 with the help of Prime Minister Margaret Thatcher who was his friend and admirer. Lord Bauer apparently earned himself this title for writing and impressing leading British politicians by claiming as he did so relentlessly that Great Britain, the principal colonizing power among European countries, had absolutely nothing to do with causing poverty in the Third World. Without evidence that he traveled extensively in Africa and Asia Lord Bauer's often demeaning characterization of the people of these continents seem mostly anecdotal, hearsay, and ethnocentric influence. Reading some of his work as I have on the Third World, I find it not inconceivable that Lord Bauer was himself in the same category of those he had described as "vicarious readers, or readers by proxy," which are those he described as not reading a book but who became aware of its contents from others (Bauer, 1981; Bauer, 1972).

The modernists, therefore, claim that the achievement of social and economic advancement in the Third World would require ridding these societies of the afore-mentioned conditions Modernists such as Walt Whitman Rostow, in his *Stages of Economic Growth A Non-Communist Manifesto* (1960) suggested that, like Europe, Third World traditional societies must undergo a sequence of five transformational stages, from the current stage of traditional societies to pre-conditions for take-off stage, take-off stage, maturity stage, and high consumption stage. This simplistic and somewhat anachronistic model suggests that development is a linear process, but that is far from being the case. The socioeconomic development process is anything but linear.

Social and Technological Dualism

Dualism is the simultaneous coexistence within the same country or economy of two different levels of development with different technological capabilities. Stated differently, dualism is the development of a small modern economy and society alongside a traditional economy and society (Higgins and Higgins, 1979). The characterization of Third World countries as "dual societies" is an attempt to isolate societies in which two distinct social systems exist synchronously within the borders of one country. Such an approach partitions individual Third World countries into "modern" and "traditional" sectors. In this dichotomy, the modern sector is characteristically small and city-based, and having distinct features such as large-scale, capital-intensive production methods and techniques supported with sophisticated modern technology from the West and Japan. The traditional sector, on the other hand, is large and where the majority of Third World citizens still live. The traditional sector is a rural, agrarian setting associated with subsistence agriculture, mom and pop handicraft and provision stores, and small-scale industries using labor-intensive techniques in most cases.

Sometimes, "technological dualism" is used as an extension of the sociological theory of dualism. However, technological dualism is used in reference to "structural unemployment" or technological unemployment, which is a condition where productive employment opportunities are limited. This condition exists not because of lack of effective demand, but because of constraints imposed by resource and technological shortage in both traditional and modern sectors. In the modern sector, technology is heavily utilized in large-scale industrial facilities and capital-intensive production processes that have limited employment-creating capability. On the other hand, labor-intensive production methods, small-scale industries, and abundant or "surplus" labor characterize the traditional sector. The existence of social and/or technological dualism is often attributed to what has been dubbed "growth without development." It is claimed that, in growth-without-development, the establishment of large-scale, capital-intensive production processes fail to produce significant improvements in other parts of a country. An instance of this is described in the following statement.

> *When a new resource is discovered, a mine opened, or a new crop introduced, one might expect a chain reaction creating jobs in other sectors of the economy, as occurred in now advanced countries. Instead, Third World countries often experience "high-growth without development." There is simply no relationship between the consequent high rate of growth, confined to the small modern sector, and the lives of the great majority of the people in the traditional sector where per capita income remains close to subsistence level and the traditional cultures remain essentially undisturbed. (Higgins and Higgins, 1979, p. 15)*

Let me end this section with a note of caution. Since no condition is permanent, the point must be made that conditions in the Third World are not static. Like the urban sprawl happening now in some developed countries, the borders of the modern sector in the Third World are gradually changing and shifting outward to incorporate areas once in the traditional sector.

Vicious Circle of poverty

The saying that Third World countries are poor because they are not developing and they are not developing because they are poor offers a simple illustration of the concept of a vicious circle of poverty. Nobel Lauriat Ragner Nurkse (1953) wrote that a vicious circle of poverty "implies a circular constellation of forces tending to act and react upon one another in such a way as to keep a poor country in a state of poverty" (p. 4). Nurkse provided one of many instances of this circular constellation of forces.

For example, a poor man may not have enough to eat; being underfed, his health may be weak; being physically weak, his work capacity is low, which means that he is poor, which means that he will not have enough to eat; and so on. A situation of this sort, relating to a country as a whole, can be summed up in the trite proposition: a country is poor because it is poor. ((p.4)

The vicious circle of poverty perhaps offers one of the plausible explanations given for the low level of capital accumulation in many Third World economies. The American Heritage Dictionary (1982) defines a vicious circle as "A situation in which the solution of one problem in a chain of circumstances creates a new problem and increases the difficulty of solving the original problem" (p.1347). In line with this definition is that by Krause (1961), who defined vicious circle as "an inextricable interrelationship of cause-and-effect that operates so as to imprison an economy in its own shortcomings" (p. 20). Third World countries are "caught in a vicious circle" as a result of the presence of a socioeconomic pattern that tends to perpetuate poverty. An example of this peculiarity among Third World countries is their low income compared with the developed countries. This characteristic conjures up yet another often used example of a vicious circle of poverty in which:

A low income means that there is a small capacity to save and thus a low rate of saving; a low rate of saving in turn means that there is a shortage of investment capital; a shortage of investment capital means that investment and consequently productivity will be low; and low productivity serves to perpetuate the low income situation. (Stockwell and Laidlaw, 1981, p. 33)

There will always be a correlation between the low income of many Third World countries and their history of colonial

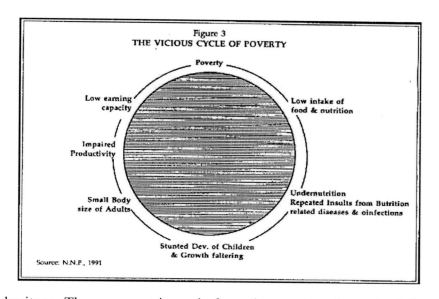

Figure 3
THE VICIOUS CYCLE OF POVERTY

Poverty

Low earning capacity

Low intake of food & nutrition

Impaired Productivity

Small Body size of Adults

Undernutrition
Repeated Insults from Nutrition related diseases & oinfections

Stunted Dev. of Children & Growth faltering

Source: N.N.P., 1991

heritage. The argument is made from time to time that colonialism ended a long time ago and that continued reference to it as an excuse for the slow progress in the Third World has become irrelevant and weak. Arguing that colonial status and post-colonialism do not inhibit material progress, Bauer (1972) wrote: "Some of the richest countries were colonies in their earlier history, notably the United States, Canada, Australia, and New Zealand; and these countries were already prosperous while they were still colonies" (p. 148). In this case Bauer failed to distinguish between two forms of colonization: First is the colonization in which the objective is to extract the resources of colonized areas for the continued advancement of the country of the colonizer. This is not the same as the form of colonization intended for settlement away from one's country of origin. In the second case you do not plunder your new country. As a Native American proverb would put it, "a frog does not drink up the pond in which it lives."

Furthermore, some Third World countries that are doing well socially and economically are often cited as proof that colonialism is no longer a factor in explaining conditions or socioeconomic problems in the Third World. However, the fact is that colonial policies were applied discriminately or inconsistently

27

among the colonies. Also, Communist Containment (i.e., The Truman Doctrine of March 12, 1947) in the Cold War era led the Unites States to directly intervene in the military and economic progress of some Third World countries and not others. That is why, given these occurrences, suggestions to stop blaming colonialism for the current state of affairs in many Third World countries are not only misinformed, but also naive and ignorant. Toye (1987) wrote on this issue the fact that one cannot rule out or deny that:

> Colonialism produced negative economic effects. Certain pre-colonial forms of economic activity were destroyed, certain colonial investments were inappropriate except within the context of colonialism itself and liberation conflicts have often burdened countries after independence with costly and turbulent military establishments. Economies have been distorted by colonialism in a way which hampers their future action for development. (p. 13)

India is often cited as a typical example of the damaging effects of colonialism, where the British destroyed budding industries and flooded the colony at the time with manufactures from metropolitan factories (Waites, 1999). As Waites (1999) pointed out, in the late 1840s up to 1860, "[t]he export of factory-produced yarn, cloth and metal utensils under-cut the market for handicraft products in the 'Third World,' leading to what many have called its 'de-industrialization'" (p. 5). However, I also strongly agree with Toye (1987) that the negative effects of colonialism

> are not insuperable; they can be struggled against successfully. In the end, whatever the extent of the economic damage of colonialism, countries which do nothing but persuade themselves that they are the victims of history will let slip such opportunities for development as they do have now. (p. 13)

True, the negative effects are surmountable and can be struggled against successfully, but the fact is that it will be a long struggle, especially with the current lopsided global economic structure in which major decisions affecting Third World countries are made in the capital cities of the industrially advanced nations, without meaningful input from Third World countries. Referring to the Uruguay Round of trade negotiations that lasted from 1986 to 1994, Nelson Mandela remarked that "the developing countries were not able to ensure that the rules accommodated their realities; it was mainly the preoccupations and problems of the advanced industrial economies that shaped the agreement" (Kwa, 1998, 2). Mandela also noted that the uniform application of rules does not make them fair because of the different circumstances of members (Kwa, 1998).

There is no denying that colonialism is a significant factor, but certainly not the only one perpetuating the vicious circle of poverty in the Third World. Other factors include their deteriorating terms of trade; declining price of raw materials from Third World countries; the invention and application of synthetic substitutes of raw materials in the industrialized world; ineptitude and venality of many Third World leaders and the elite group; the use of bribery by multinational corporations as a means of circumventing bureaucratic red tape and influencing Third World government officials; the diversion of public and loan funds to private foreign accounts by Third World officials; the use of public and loan funds for unproductive purposes such as construction of palaces, ostentatious birthday parties for government officials celebrated with imported and very expensive, custom-made beverages, purchasing expensive jewelry for the spouses of government officials; the marginalizing impact of globalization on the Third World despite its benefits; Third World external debt burden; the monopoly of international decision making by the industrially advanced nations; certain actions of the industrial countries that are tantamount to neocolonialism; political instability in many Third World countries; and a host of others.

Referring to the Third World, the late Prime Minister of Jamaica wrote long ago that "in all too many instances endemic corruption, wasteful and extravagant public projects, rejection of principles of participatory governance, and inept government intervention in the domestic marketplace combine with turbulence in the world economy to stifle economic growth and maturity" (Manley, 1990, p. 41).

Can Third World countries successfully emerge from the quagmire of the vicious circle? Yes, of course, but it will require a lot of hard work, social discipline, strong political will, a change in the global economic structure to ensure a level playing field for all, recognizing and incorporating the ideas and needs of Third World countries in global decision making, and a radical change in the attitude of both developing and developed countries. These countries have to galvanize their collective efforts to alter the prevailing form of globalization and global division of labor, which tend to disproportionately favor the industrialized nations. Third World countries need to overcome the lingering and dilatory effects of colonialism and get on with the urgent business of nation building and national development. I am in complete agreement with Stanford University Professor Gerald M. Meier, who wrote that an economics of resentment against an erstwhile colonial relationship is not at the very least a helpful substitute for the type of "economics needed to promote development. Economic development cannot be legislated or voted on as can political independence. There is merit in the economist's advice to governments of developing countries that 'good economics is good for you'" (Meier, 1984, p. 206).

Exporters of Raw materials

A common citation in the literature is the claim that Third World countries export unprocessed agricultural products and mineral resources to the industrialized countries, from where they import manufactured goods. This assertion may have had validity in the early years following their independence from former colonial powers. As former colonies of European countries, many Third World countries inherited economies that were dependent on agricultural production and mineral extraction. As Hadjor (1992) described it,

> *The role of the colonies was to complement the economic requirements of the metropolitan powers. The needs of domestic development were a matter of indifference to them. In many cases, imperialism directly discouraged internal economic development since they wanted to prevent the emergence of new competitors. Colonies were thus assigned the role of providing cheap raw materials and acting as markets for manufactured goods from the metropolitan powers. (pp. 69-70)*

Diamond mining, south Africa

That being the case, it was not surprising that the new nations emerged after their independence as exporters mainly of unprocessed raw materials and mineral resources to the developed nations. However, the economies of Third World countries have not been static since independence; they have been going beyond the stage of exporting primary commodities and increasingly taking part in the global production of manufactures, as well as experiencing increasing share of the relevant markets (Revel, 1988). In the mid to late 1950s, the percentage of Third World output classed as having originated in raw materials production very much exceeded that regarded as having manufacturing origins, with ranges of 40% to 60% and 10% to 15%, respectively, being typical at the time (Krause, 1961). However, the output composition of raw materials and manufactured goods changed between 1965 and 1988, as the share of manufactured goods in total Third World exports increased from 16% to 64% (The World Bank, 1990). Better yet, "in 1965 manufactured goods accounted for only 16% of the exports from the Third World, but by the early 1990s they had reached around 66%" (Mason, 1997, pp. 457-458). Hadjor (1992) provided more detail in stating that "of total Third World exports more than half (60%) is now of manufactured goods, 22% is fuel, including petroleum, and only 17% is other primary products, the exports which are most traditionally associated with the Third World..." (p. 111). It must be added that a sizable amount of these manufactured goods come from the newly industrializing countries (NICs). Seventy-five percent of these manufactured exports originate from seven countries, of which the four NICs of East Asia accounted for 50% by the end of the 1980s (Kurian, 1992; The World Bank, 1991). More recent data also show that developing countries, like the developed, export more manufactured goods than primary products at 56% of their total, or 14% of world exports (University of CA, at Santa Cruz, 2005).

Third World Debt Burden

Third World debt generally referred to as 'debt crisis' surfaced as a major international issue in the early 1980s. This indebtedness of the Third World to the advanced nations, multilateral agencies, and private financial institutions is, unfortunately, a feature that more Third World countries share in common than anything else. Third World debt as of 2004 was estimated at more than $2.5 trillion, resulting a debt-servicing cost to the Third World of over $375 billion per year. This cost of servicing their indebtedness to the developed world "is more than all third world spending on health and education, and twenty times what developing countries receive annually in foreign aid" (Perkins, 2004, p. xxii

Third World debt is made up of multilateral, bilateral, and private commercial bank loans. Multilateral loans are those made by agencies such as the World Bank, International Monetary Fund, the African Development Bank, Inter-American Development Bank, and the Asian Development Bank. They are multilateral in the sense that they extend loans to many countries simultaneously. Bilateral loans are loans from one government to another, made on one-on-one basis. Private commercial banks, also known as The London Club, loans are those disbursed by such global financial giants as Citibank, JP Morgan Chase Bank, and their counterparts in Europe.

Much of the bilateral loans are made with strings attached, or the so-called "tied" aid. Bilateral loans are not made out of altruism but based on enlightened self-interest. The recipient government or country is required to use the loan money to purchase goods and services exclusively from the country of the loan-granting government. Usually the money never leaves the country of the loan-granting government, as it serves to boost the domestic economy. This practice, among other things, deprives the recipient country the freedom to purchase the products and services it needs at competitive prices. Under these circumstances costs usually are artificially inflated so that less products and services are acquired as a result. This situation was well described years ago by Gaud (1968) using the United States to illustrate how most bilateral loans work.

The biggest single misconception about the foreign aid program is that we send money abroad. We don't. Foreign aid consists of American equipment, raw materials, expert services, and food—all provided for specific development projects which we ourselves review and approve....Ninety-three percent of the Aid funds are spent directly in the United States to pay for these things. Just last year

some 4,000 American firms in 50 states $1.3 billion
in AID funds for products supplied as part of the
foreign aid program. (p.603)

One way that the multilateral financial institutions are used to get Third World countries in debt is through the corporatocracy, a powerful alliance of United States biggest corporations, government, and too-big-to-fail banks. The corporatocracy enlists the services of agents known Economic Hit Men (EHMs) to get Third World leaders to agree to accept loans from The World Bank and its sister organizations for infrastructure development in their countries. Targeted for debt ensnarement are especially those Third World countries possessing mineral resources like oil, which our United States corporations desire. Examples of favored infrastructure include electric generating plants, highways, ports, airports, and/or industrial parks. These loans come with conditions binding on receiving Third World countries. For example, the various infrastructure projects must be built by United States engineering and construction companies. "In essence, most of the money never leaves the United States; it is simply transferred from banking offices in Washington to engineering offices in in New York, Houston, and San Francisco" (Perkins, 2004, p. xx). The loan amounts are usually so large that the debtor country usually defaults on its loan repayment. Under the control of the creditor, the defaulting Third World country would acquiesce to whatever the creditor demands, which usually includes access to the debtor country's oil or the installation of the United States military base in the country. Regardless of these impositions and the fact that the loan monies never left the United States, the poor country owes every penny of the loan plus rapidly rising interest amounts (Perkins, 2007; 2004).

The third major source of Third World debt is that owed to Western private banks, also known as The London Club. With the inception of the energy crisis of 1973 and 1979, oil price went up dramatically enabling oil-producing countries to amass unprecedented wealth of oil revenue. Hardly able to spend this newly found wealth fast enough, Third World oil-producing countries deposited their petro-dollars in private banks in the developed world. Subsequent decline in interest rates and the eminence of global economic depression became the incentive for these banks to engage in reckless lending of these petro-dollars in their custody mostly to governments of poor countries, with little or no scrutiny to determine countries' ability to repay their loans. These banks also believed that debt owed by a sovereign country or "sovereign debt" "carried minimum risks of default" (Toye, 1987, p. 2). The eventual fall in the price of oil and elevated interest rates exacerbated the debt burden of these poor countries, forcing many to default on their loan repayment. That was when The London Club enlisted the assistance of The International Monetary Fund (IMF) and World Bank to initiate Structural Adjustment Programs of the 1980's as a condition for poor countries to receive further loans with which to be able to continue repayment of loan principal and interests, also known as debt servicing. The adverse impact of SAPs on development in the Third World is welled documented and will not be treated in any detail here.

The paradox of development loans is that the debt burden has become so cumbersome that it is now constitutes an obstacle to development, which they are supposed to promote. Revenues generated from successful investment are used to make interest payments on loans instead of being invested in social programs that improve living standards. To illustrate, the West African country of Nigeria borrowed $5 billion and has paid $16 billion to date but still owes $32 billion. It is important to point out that the sad reality in this case is that Nigeria spends more money each year trying to keep up with its interest payment obligation than it spends on education" (Iowa State University, 2005). The good news is that in June 2005 the G8 (Group of 8) Britain, Italy, Germany, Russia, France, Japan, Canada, and the United States reached an agreement to write off $40 billion owed by 18 of the world's poorest countries. This amount comprises the multilateral debts of Benin, Bolivia, Burkina Faso, Ethiopia, Ghana, Guyana,

Honduras, Madagascar, Mali, Mauritania, Mozambique, Nicaragua, Niger, Rwanda, Senegal, Tanzania, Uganda, and Zambia owed to the World Bank, the International Monetary Fund (IMF), and the African Development Bank (All I need, n. d.).

Population Concerns

As noted in chapter one, three-quarters of humanity reside in the Third World. In a world of over six billion people, this comes to about 4.7 billion people living on two-thirds of the surface of our planet earth.

Rapid growth in population has not always been the case in the Third World. Many believe that there is a population problem in Africa, Asia, and Latin America, but this is a relatively recent development. Kurian (1992) observed that "until the 20th century, the real rate

Three-quarters of humanity reside in the Third World.

of population growth was held in check by a high mortality rate" (p. ix). What we now call population explosion in the Third World is a phase early in the development of countries that generally reflects improving access to basic needs in a society, medical care, and general socioeconomic conditions. Accelerating population growth in the Third World has came with declining mortality rates and increasing life expectancy the number of years a newborn human child is expected to live given that the same conditions or circumstances of mortality at the time of the child's birth stay unchanged for the child's entire life. Rapidly declining death rates since 1950, at least until the AIDS epidemic, and the fact that people are living longer today, are indicative of improving nutrition, sanitation, personal hygiene, and medical services in Third World societies. Revel (1988) wrote that the "demographic explosion is initially a consequence of progress, which the multiplication of the active population further accelerates...It is only when a higher level of well-being has been achieved that demographic stagnation, coupled with a long life expectancy, spontaneously sets in" (p. 38). Due mostly to a deliberate control of the birth rate, several so-called Third World countries are now beginning to enter this phase as did the countries of southern Europe some decades ago (Revel, 1988). One would agree with the preceding statements, which are in accord with the theory of demographic transition, which has been widely explained and will not be repeated here.

Birth rates in the countries of the Third World have been lowered from an average of over six children per family in the 1960s to an average of about 3.5 children. Roughly half of this decline is from the adoption of contraceptives, the use of which has grown about five-fold over the past several decades to include 55% of married couples in the Third World (Florman, 1994).This is a remarkable change from the 8% who used contraceptives in 1965 when they were averaging more than six children per family (Sinding and Segal, 1991). In a matter of sixteen years, from 1960 to 1975, more than thirty governments of Third World countries adopted official policies and programs aimed at encouraging family planning and control (Kurian, 1992). A World Bank estimate of $3 billion is spent each year by Third World countries on family planning and related activities like demographic surveys and public information campaign. Six hundred billion of this amount comes from some developed nations in support of the effort (Sinding and Segal, 1991).

It will be a mistake to close this section without pointing out that the claim of population explosion in the Third World does not reflect a consensus. There are skeptics who challenge the notion of population and argue that there is no population problem but a distribution problem in the Third World. The proponents of this school of thought contend that too many people live in one area while other locations are scantily populated. While I do not dismiss the fact that there are population concerns in the Third World, I believe that hunger, starvation, and malnutrition are not always the result of over population. It is not revealing anything new that most Third World countries have outgrown the agricultural technology they use today. Many of these countries are still using technologies of bygone ages, which were once appropriate when the population was small. With an upgrade to modern technology, Third World countries would feed their citizens without much difficulty. Finally, one must bear in mind that most Third World countries are artificial creations carved out along arbitrary borders by former colonial powers and forcing people of different ethnicity, culture, religion, and creed into one country. Burundi and Rwanda are examples that come to mind. This has created a condition in which hunger, starvation, and malnutrition are not due to food shortage but the result of human cruelty, wickedness, and heartlessness perpetrated by the ethnic or tribal group in power against members of other ethnic or tribal groups.

Political Instability

Everywhere in the Third World, especially in Africa and Latin America, civil unrest is devastating economies and subjecting citizens to excruciating hardship. Political instability in the Third World is often dismissed as a common attribute of traditional societies, even though the rampant social unrest in these regions was uncommon prior to European imperialism. Governments in the Third World, particularly those in the African continent, inherited irrational boundaries that crossed ethnic lines and separated people with common ancestry, language, culture, and name. Testimonies of colonial intrusion and the creation of social structures conducive to political instability are offered in the writings of various development researchers and scholars. A couple of examples will suffice. First, Dickenson, Clarke, Gould, Hodgkiss, Prothero, Siddle, Smith, & Thomas-Hope (1983) wrote:

> *Important political consequences of colonization lay in the balkanization of regions through the creation of national boundaries bearing little relationship to pre-existing tribal or cultural zones. Unrelated, even hostile ethnic and tribal groups were brought together and a homogeneous colonial authority imposed on them. With independence, the emergent states have in some cases been divided and disrupted to the point of open and persistent warfare as tribal conflict is exacerbated by political competitiveness and the domination of one group over the rest. (p. 41)*

O'Neil (1992) was expressing something similar in the following statement.

> *Numerous Third World states are artificial entities created by colonial experience. People having different tribal loyalties, languages, religions and historical experiences often are impressed into an artificial union while the sole unit to which personal loyalty attaches is often the family, tribe, or village...Few new nations are culturally homogeneous; many are torn by cultural divisions that encourage violent disruptions. (pp. 349-350)*

Given such indiscriminate amalgamations carried out during the colonial era, the social and political unrest in many Third World countries hardly comes as a surprise.

Adverse Climate Conditions

A common argument in the literature is that since a majority of Third World countries lives in tropical and sub-tropical regions, the people, soil, agriculture, and productivity are inhibited by intense heat and humidity. The people are weakened and susceptible to ill health and, consequently, their productivity is minimal; the soil is impoverished as humus or topsoil is destroyed faster than it forms; and agricultural yields are hardly anything to write home about. These claims are mostly generalizations that can only be partially true given the diversity and vastness of the Third World. It is for this reason that Welsh and Butorin (1990) made the following observation:

> Over the last two to three decades, many myths have grown about the tropics. It is often stated that tropical soils are very low in fertility, climate conditions extreme, plant and animal pest problems are insurmountable, human health problems are serious, etc. While these assertions are true to varying degrees depending on location and level of development...it is unscientific to generalize about vast areas with such different physical, social, and economic conditions. (p. 194)

What we know about the tropical climate is rather minuscule in comparison with the knowledge resulting from more than two centuries of research on the temperate climate. It is this accumulated knowledge that aided the temperate countries' adaptation by giving rise to numerous inventions and innovations. I often wonder what, for instance, would be the nature of the discussion today if the tropical countries were developed instead of the temperate zone countries, and if most of the research had been focused on tropical conditions. It would not be an exaggeration in this sense to imagine that the future prospect of the "less developed" temperate zones would be as bleak as is now the case with the tropical countries of the Third World. Again, here are the thoughts of Welsh and Butorin (1992) on the issue.

> *If circumstances had been reversed, prospects for temperate zone development might well seem dim. Yet, as we know, such speculations would be false, stemming directly from lack of knowledge of how to develop the region appropriately. We now face the same problem with tropical countries, since we still do not know enough about tropical plants, many of which can be successfully exploited as sources of food, fiber, forage, and fuel. We need more information on tropical soil and how to obtain sustainable agricultural yields. Scientific research capacity has improved tremendously during the past two to three decades, and thus it should not take us another two centuries to contrive sustainable development processes for the tropics. (Welsh and Butorin, 1990, pp. 194-195)*

As the temperate countries have shown, perceived climate induced constraints are not by nature insuperable. Human beings are by nature endowed with the capacity to adapt to and be sustained by their environment. Attempts by different societies to adapt to their natural environment usually start out with contrivances that may be called primitive, but these contrivances are transformed technologically as societies evolve. As I have already mentioned in this book, communities, societies, or countries have evolved historically as they apply the type of technology that reflects their level of development and factor endowment. The changes that take place as societies attempt to "tame" nature occur at a fast pace in some societies while at a slow pace in others. Tropical climate conditions of many Third World countries are solvable with relevant scientific research efforts.

Agricultural Economy

Whereas industrial production is the mainstay of the economies of the developed countries, the economies of most Third World countries are based on agriculture. This can be seen from the proportion of the labor force in agricultural and industrial production, as well as from the sector by sector composition of the gross domestic product (GDP). The figures from the 1994 Human Development Report show that from 1990 to 1992 an average of 9% of the workforce in the industrial nations and 58% in Third World nations were engaged in agriculture (UNDP, 1994). This disparity is even more pronounced when individual countries are compared. For instance, less than 3% of the population in the United States earns their living working in agriculture, while it is 72% for the poorest countries of the Third World. Agriculture contributes an average of 32% to the GDP of developing countries, and only 7% for the more affluent economies of the developed world (World Bank, 1991; Stockwell and Laidlaw, 1981). As the World Bank (1991) pointed out, "Development has almost always involved a shift in the sectoral composition of output. Agriculture's share in production and employment which is typically high in the early stages begins to decline, and that of manufacturing industry to increase" (p. 32). In 1965 the industrial sector's annual

contribution to the GDP in the Third World was 27%, and that of agriculture was 47%. "There are similar shifts in the sectoral shares of employment...although agriculture remains the biggest employer in many developing countries" (World Bank, 1991, p. 32). In 1965 the percentage of the labor force in agriculture in Third World countries as a whole was about 72%, and 83% for the poorest countries.

Concluding Remarks

While it is true that many Third World countries lag behind the developed countries in social and economic terms, the improvements they have made cannot be denied. The per capita GDP in the less developed economies as a whole has nearly doubled over the last generation, having grown faster than the United Kingdom during the Industrial Revolution, faster than the United States in the period of rapid growth as it came to economic maturity, and faster than Japan during the prewar growth spurt (Summers, 1992). Life expectancy among Third World countries increased 27% from 46.2 years in 1960 to 63 years in 1992 (UNDP, 1994). The adult literacy rate for Third World nations as a whole increased from 46% in 1970 to 65% in 1990 (UNDP, 1993). However, these improvements do not get much attention in part because the figures have remained lower than those for the industrialized countries. For this and other possible reasons, most discussions about Third World countries often are in the form that suggests unchanging conditions.

References

The American heritage dictionary (2nd ed.). (1982). Boston, MA: Houghton Mifflin Company

Ambrose, S. (1999, August). Multilateral debt [Electronic version]. Multilateral Debt, 4 (21), p. 1

Bauer, P. T. (1981). Equality, the Third World and economic delusion. Cambridge, MA: Harvard University Press.

Bauer, P. T. (1972). Dissent on development: Studies and debates in development economics. Cambridge, MA: Harvard University Press.

Dickerson, J. P.; Clarke, C. G.; Gould, W. T. S.; Hodgkiss, A. G.; Prothero, R. M.; Siddle, D. J.; Smith, C. T.; & Thomas-Hope, E. M.; & (1983). *A geography of the Third World.* New York: NY: Methuen & Co.

All I Need. (n. d.). G8 immediately writes off 40 billion dollars in Third World debt. Retrieved January 16, 2006, from http://www.theallineed.com/news/0506/115549.htm

Florman, S. G. (1994, October). Overpopulation alarm. *Technology Review, 97(7), 65.*

Hadjor, K. B. (1992). Dictionary of Third World terms. London: England: I. B. Tauris & Co. Ltd.

Higgins, B. H. & Higgins, J.D. (1979). *Economic development of a small planet.* New York, NY: Norton

Iowa State University (2005, May 19). Third-World nations in need of debt relief. *Iowa State Daily via U-Wire*

Krause, W. (1961). *Economic development: the underdeveloped world and the American interest.* Belmont, CA: Wadsworth Publishing Company, Inc.

Kurian, G. (Ed.). (1992). *Atlas of the Third World* (2nd ed.) New York, NY: Facts On File, Inc.

Kwa, A. (1998, November). WTO and developing countries. News, 3(37). Retrieved from http://www.fpif.org/briefs/vol3/v3n37wto-body.html

Manley, M. (1990, Fall). Southern needs. *Foreign Policy,* 80, 40-51

Mason, M. (1997). *Development and disorder: A history of the Third World since 1945.* Hanover, NH: University Press of New England.

McAffee, K. (1990, June). Why the Third World goes hungry; selling cheap and buying dear. *Commonweal,* 117(12), 380-385.

Meier, G. M. (1984). *Emerging from poverty; the economic that really matters.* New York, NY: Oxford University Press

Nurkse, R. (1953). *Problems of capital formation in underdeveloped countries*. New York, NY: Oxford University Press

O'Neal, D. J. (1992, Summer). Edmund Burke, Karl Marx, and the contemporary Third World. Modern Age, 349-358

Revel, J. (1988, February). From rags to riches? Economics in the Third World. *Encounter*, 80(2), 37-38

Rostow, W. W. (1960). *The stages of economic growth: A noncommunist manifesto*. London: Cambridge University Press.

Schaefer, R. T. & Lamm, R. P. (1989). *Sociology* (3rd ed.). New York, NY: McGraw-Hill, Inc.

Sinding, S. W. & Segal, S. J. (1991, December 19). Birth-rate news. *The New York Times*, p. A31 (L)

Stockwell, E. G. & Laidlaw, K. A. (1981). *Third World development: problems and prospects*. Chicago, IL: Nelson-Hall, Inc.

Summers, L. H. (1992, March). The challenge of development. *Finance and Development,* 6-9

Toye, J. (1987). *Dilemmas of development: reflections on the counter-revolution in development theory and policy*. New York, NY: Basil Blackwell Inc.

United Nations Development Program (1993). Human development report. New York, NY: Oxford University Press

United Nations Development Program (1994). *Human development report*. New York, NY: Oxford University Press

University of California, Santa Cruz (2005). *International trade flows and inequality*. The University of California Atlas of Global Inequality. Retrieved from http://ucatlas.ucsc-edu/trade_theme.php

Waites, B. (1999). *Europe and Third World: from Colonialism to decolonization c. 1500-1998*. New York, NY: St. Martin's Press

Welsh, B. W. W. & Butorin, P. (Eds.). (1990). *Dictionary of development* (vols. 1 & 2). New York, NY: Garland Publishing, Inc.

The World Bank (1990). *World development report* 1990. New York, NY: Oxford University Press

The World Bank (1991). *World development report* 1991. New York, NY: Oxford University Press

Chapter THREE

Development Reconsidered

Introduction

When the ex-colonies of Africa and Asia joined their Latin American counterparts in achieving political independence as sovereign states after World War II, the task of nation building and national development, for the first time, became the responsibility of the new nations and their native leaders. Aware of the challenging task ahead, the new leaders, most of whom had played active roles in different nationalist movements for independence, were determined to prove to their former colonizers in particular that they were capable of self-rule and managing their own affairs. Most of these new leaders were also recipients of Western education, and so came as no surprise when many of them turned to Western economists for advice on socioeconomic development (Meier, 2001). Also not surprising, at least to the unbiased, was the advice they received.

Since the attainment of independence, Third World countries have been at the receiving end of foreign aid and have been the testing ground of development strategies crafted in the West. The end of World War II came with renewed interest in the growth strategy of development. Economic growth was either erroneously or selfishly promoted in an entirely different world order as a synonym of development, and the key to social and economic development in the Third World. The notion strongly advanced mostly by modernist theorists was that Third World countries needed modernization in their general outlook if they are to achieve economic growth.

According to the modernization school of thought, 'traditional' societies are handicapped by superstitions, factiousness, fatalism, venality, laziness, deviousness, cruelty, and other sentiments and practices considered not supportive of growth. Modernizing Third World economies was, therefore, proposed as a means of eliminating these traits and as a necessary prerequisite of growth. With modernization underway, growth in Third World economies would inevitably result from industrialization induced by capital accumulation, technology transfer from the West, exports, global trade, the assistance of Western technical experts, and infrastructure development. It is important to mention here that Third World countries were designated late-comers to development that did not have to reinvent the wheel because the required factors for their industrialization would be made available to them for purchase from the industrialized world. This approach to the industrialization of Third World countries would of course have the undermining effect of ensuring they would not acquire the indigenous technological capability to invent, innovate, adapt technology, and set up production facilities by themselves according to their interests and needs. The putative economic growth, it was envisioned, would translate into gains in productivity, the gross domestic product (GDP), and other macroeconomic interests. This in turn would result in rising per capita income the neoclassical economist's established yardstick for measuring development.

The purpose of this chapter is to discuss the challenges of Third World development and the need to move beyond the development-as-growth basis of the conventional development strategy. The numerous problems facing the Third World can no longer rely entirely on growth and the trickle-down mechanism that attempt to resolve them indirectly. An integrated and more effective strategy for this purpose must be articulated from a broad view of development and must be multi-pronged and direct. As has already been explained in chapter one and will be in subsequent chapters,

Third World countries themselves are not homogeneous. Ideas that are appropriate to the Indian sub-continent, for instance, are often not practical in the African continent. Even within Africa itself, there are important differences between countries, due to differences in customs, colonial experience, geography, and culture. Given this reality, no single development strategy is likely to be appropriate to every country (Toye, 1987).

The Development Discourse

Long ago, Karl Marx had remarked that "the country that is more developed industrially only shows, to the less developed, the image of its future" (Mason, 1997, p. 17). This statement suggests, among other things, that the attraction of the development-as-growth paradigm is based strictly on its past history of success in the developed world. Evidence of this effectiveness in our time would include the interventionist economics that virtually solved the problem of mass unemployment in Europe and the United States dubbed the New Deal in the United States and the resounding success of the U.S.-led Marshall Plan in Western Europe and Japan after the Second World War. Due in no small measure to the success of the Marshall Plan, Western economists and other development planners assumed very optimistically that enlisting similar enterprise in the newly independent Third World economies would have the same outcome (Adelman, 2001). The growth strategy also gained in appeal from the work of Walt Whitman Rostow, a former Massachusetts Institute of Technology professor of history of English industrialization and a modernist scholar. In his book, *The Stages of Economic Growth: A Non-Communist Manifesto*, Rostow (1960) outlined a linear approach to development involving a sequence of five stages that postcolonial countries must follow to 'modernize' and industrialize. A modern society is said to be characterized by "typical social patterns of demography, urbanization and literacy; typical economic patterns of production and consumption, investment, trade and government finance; and typical psychological attributes of rationality, ascriptive identity and achievement motivation" (Toye, 1987, p. 11). Emphasizing foreign aid, modernization, predictably, required the active involvement of Western experts as guides and advisers. In his book, Rostow (1960) likened the process of economic growth to that of an aircraft slowly gaining speed along the runway before a "rapid surge towards 'industrial' take-off into the clear sky of sustained economic growth" (Dickenson, J. P., Clarke, C. G., Gould, W. T. S., Prothero, R. M., Siddle, D. J., Smith, C. T., Hope, E. M. T., and Hodgkiss, A. G., 1983, p. 15). The translation of this analogy is that Third World countries will move from traditional societies to acquire the necessary precondition for take off to a modern economy, then taking off into modern economies, which will be followed by the drive to maturity, and subsequently the emergence of a high mass consumption economy (Rostow, 1960). Again, the impetus for this sense of optimism is to be found in the erroneous reasoning that these stages worked for the Western countries and should have the same outcome in the new nations. This view of development as a linear process is a simplistic model in the sense that it is "based on too limited a view of the European Industrial Revolution" (Dickenson, J. P., et al, 1983, p. 16). One has to be reminded that the Western countries developed in a different international context than what obtains today. In other words, applying the stages-of-economic-growth strategy totally as formulated may be anachronistic. A fair criticism of the modernization theory has to do with its apparent disregard for the part that culture plays in development. Kamrava (2000) wondered whether cultural peculiarities in the Third World are so insignificant as to prompt it to follow a similar tradition-modernity trajectory that Europe did. He argued that "Simply to assume that such resonant phenomena as religion, tribalism, ethnicity, caste and other culture-driven forces will wither away under the weight of modernity or careful political crafting is, at best, foolhardy" (p. 31). In short, the proponents of modernization worked toward devising mechanisms and procedures that would have Third World societies fit a preexisting model that embodied the structures and functions of modernity. This goal, however, ignores the fact that change is a process rooted in the interpretation of each society's history and cultural tradition (Escobar, 1995).

These initial variant of the growth strategy based on interventionist economics originated from the work of the famous British economist John Maynard Keynes, generally known as Keynesian economics. Keynesian economics rests in the belief that the free play of the money markets would lead to booms and slumps of increasing severity, so that in the modern world no sophisticated social, political, and economic system could survive in the absence of prudent government-administered regulation of the economy. Keynes believed in the efficacy of capitalism, but he also believed that economic growth was more likely to be sustained and to benefit more people with the wise intervention of the government to complement market forces (Dickenson, J. P., et al, 1983).

However, Keynes's interventionist economics came under attack in the 1970s, especially by the neo-classical economists, who argue, among other things, that Keynesian economics was critical of capitalism, unfettered global trade, and placed undue emphasis on the importance of physical capital formation in economic processes.

It is the belief of neo-classical economists that the interaction of market forces, acting as if with an "invisible hand" will ensure economic equilibrium and stability in the economy without meddling government intervention. The problems of the Third World, as the neo-classical economist see it, are due to misguided development policies influenced by Keynesian economics and not a "legacy of colonial history or the reflection of global structural inequalities" (Toye, 1987, p. 25). They believe in "free trade" and promoted its cause on the basis of countries doing what they do best as prescribed in the theory of comparative advantage. They argue that free trade based on comparative advantage will produce "harmony of interest" for all countries concerned, because wealth from growth will trickle-down to the poor in the long run. This faith in economic growth and the trickle-down mechanism derives from past development theories, one of which states that inequality, characteristic of the early stages of development, is subsequently ameliorated in the course of economic growth (World Bank, 2000; UNDP, 1996). The claim made that the trickle-down effect will ensue "in the long run" was aptly dismissed by John Maynard Keynes himself, who observed that "in the long run we are all dead" (Singer, 1984, p. 277). Be that as it may, the neo-classical academics and their political advocates and decision-makers gained the upper hand in the 1980s, relegating the Keynesian interventionist economics to relative obscurity. As an essential part of the whole package of neoclassical approach to development, the World Bank and the International Monetary Fund (IMF) introduced the Structural Adjustment Programs (SAPs) in 1980.

Its weaknesses notwithstanding, the growth-as-development approach and its accompanying trickle-down economics was embraced with enthusiasm by governments and the multilateral agencies. In 1961 the UN General Assembly passed Resolution 1710 (XVI) designating the 1960s as the First Development Decade. The objective of the First Development decade was:

To accelerate progress toward self-sustaining growth of the economy of the individual nations and their social advancement so as to attain in each underdeveloped country a substantial increase in the rate of growth, with each country setting its own target, taking as the objective a minimum rate of growth of aggregate national income of 5 percent at the end of the decade. (Welsh and Butorin, 1990, p. 426; Meier, 1984, p. 43)

Subsequent decades have been designated in ascending numerical order. the Second Development Decade corresponds to the period 1970 to 1979, the Third Development Decade 1980 to 1989, the Fourth Development Decade 1990 to 1999, and the Fifth Development Decade 2000 to 2009. As the decades have succeeded each other, social conditions in the Third World have not improved as expected. In fact, the record of accomplishments has been so unimpressive in some regions that the development decades have at times been contemptuously called "decades of disappointment." This disappointment compounded by deteriorating terms of trade and fluctuating commodity prices, engendered calls for a New International Economic Order (NIEO). Terms of trade compare the cost of what a country or nation must import and what it realizes as income from its exports to other countries. Terms of trade deteriorate when a country sells cheap and buys dear; that is, a situation where the cost of a country's imports rises faster than its income from exports.

The NIEO was originally proposed at the Algiers Conference of Non-aligned Movement (NAM) in 1973. The Group of 77 took up this initiative that same year and campaigned for its implementation with the support of the UN Conference on Trade and Development (UNCTAD) (Young, 1993). A majority of the member States at the Special Session of the UN General Assembly voted in favor of the Charter of Economic Rights and Duties of States on December 12, 1974, promulgating the ideology of NIEO as a result (Mason, 1997; Mittelman and Pasha, 1997). The aim of the NIEO was to initiate "what was considered a fairer distribution of global wealth by negotiating a new set of rules for economic relations in the field of commodities, world finance, industry, trade, and technology transfer" (Welsh and Butorin, 1990, p. 710). Interestingly, those who either abstained or voted against the measure were the industrialized countries whose contributions constituted 95 percent of the UN budget (Mason, 1997). Worth mentioning is the remark attributed to the United States representative at the UN, John A. Scali, in rejecting the outcome of the vote: 'When the rule of the majority becomes the tyranny of the majority, the minority will cease to respect and obey it' (Mason 1997). Without the support of the industrialized nations, the NIEO was never implemented.

By the end of the first development decade many Third World countries - e.g., Brazil, Kenya, Mexico, Pakistan, South Korea, Syria, and Thailand were showing annual growth rates of 5 percent and above. For instance, Kenya, Brazil, and South Korea reported annual growth rates of 7.1, 8, and 8.5 percent respectively. In spite of these impressive gains, poverty, hardship, unemployment, and inequality persisted. Economic growth along with its trickle-down theory was not leaving up to its promise to benefit the poor. Instead, the proceeds of growth went to a few mostly well-to-do individuals. It is not surprising then that many observers noted that modernization benefits only the elites of Third World countries (Dickenson, L. P., et al, 1983, p. 16). It must be stated in fairness to the neoclassical academics, however, that the votaries of the trickle-down theory only claimed it would help the poor "in the long run." In any event, over fifty years of Third World development effort has yet to validate this theory. Critics have argued that it is morally wrong for millions of people to be facing insufferable hardship on account of a protracted and uncertain future relief. Of the 4.4 billion people in developing countries about 1.5 billion live on less than US$1 a day (at 1985 prices) (Meier, 2001; World Bank, 2000). It is important perhaps to note that classical economists, from Adam Smith to Karl Marx, quite unlike their neoclassical successors, were very concerned about growth and distribution. According to Meier (1984), Adam Smith warned that 'No society can surely be flourishing and happy, of which the far greater part of the members are poor and miserable' (p. 4). Referring to the outcome of more than a decade of rapid growth in the Third World after the first Development Decade, a former World Bank Vice President observed:

It is now clear that more than a decade of rapid growth in underdeveloped countries has been little or no benefit to perhaps a third of their population. Although the average per capita income of the Third World has increased by 50 percent since 1960, this growth has been very unequally distributed among countries, regions, within countries, and socioeconomic groups. (Meier, 1984, p. 161)

Persistent social problems in the Third World despite the rapid economic growth experienced in several countries, continued use of per capita GDP as the sole measure of development has come under attack. Not only is this measure silent on increasing cases of human suffering, but also silent on the pattern of income distribution, growing inequality between and within countries, rapid depletion of nonrenewable resources, and accompanying environmental damage. Basu (2001) put it more succinctly:

To maximize income growth, environmental considerations were left to languish on the sidelines; the standard of living was often allowed to slide; large inequalities between classes, regions, and genders were ignored; and poverty was tolerated more than should have been in the rush to generate maximum growth (p. 64).

True development should not be taking place simultaneously with escalating social problems. Unrelenting social problems suggest, among other things, that there is more to development than expanding GDP and rising per capita income. Decades of experience seem to suggest that growth may be necessary but not a sufficient condition for development. Meier (2001) referred to a new growth theory in which "development" is defined as "growth plus change and that change implies other objectives beyond simple GDP growth.

Emphasis on "quality growth," or a desired pattern of growth, incorporates broader criteria of development such as poverty reduction, distributional equity, environmental protection" (p. 24). It has taken more than five decades of development-as-growth mindset, to observe that "economic growth does not assist the poor if it does not reach the poor" (Meier, 1984, p. 29). We know now that in the absence of a concerted effort to deal with the issue of distribution simultaneously, growth by itself is at the very least an effective antidote for the debilitating problem of poverty in the Third World. More recently, the World Bank (2000) noted that one of the lessons from fifty years of development experience is that "growth does not trickle down; development must address human needs directly" (p. 1).

Pointing out the weaknesses of a growth strategy is not to suggest that it should be supplanted or that it is not necessary. Growth is certainly essential. Growth achieved within the context of unfettered trade constitutes the catalyst driving the current globalization, which has the overarching goal of integrating the Third World into the global economy. As most people probably know, the rise of the West to social and economic preeminence is invariably attributed to the growth strategy. This faith in the neoclassical growth paradigm is so strong that any suggestion that it could possibly be one of the structural causes of the present global disparity in the distribution of wealth would be inconceivable for many of us in the Western world. As was noted earlier, neo-classical economists readily attribute present Third World problems to Keynesian economics; for instance, they posit that:

The problems of the Third World were not a legacy of colonial history or the reflection of global structural inequalities: they were the result of current policies erroneously undertaken in the deluded belief that they would foster development. Moreover, the policies themselves would not be altered as long as the policy-makers in developing countries continued to stand in the shadow of Keynes. (Toye, 1987, p. 25)

In any case, the UNDP (1999) has cautioned that "globalization is too important to be left as unmanaged as it is at present, because it has the capacity to do extraordinary harm as well as good" (p. v). Not only does globalization have positive, innovative, and dynamic aspects, but it also has negative, disruptive, and marginalizing aspects (UNDP, 1999). It is no exaggeration that globalization, enforced with uncompromising macroeconomic leaning, tends to increase Third World vulnerability with its greater focus on exogenous rather than endogenous growth. Common sense tells us that endogenous growth induced through enhanced domestic human capital would do more in terms of fostering self-sustained progress in the Third World.

Interestingly, China, India, and Malaysia three of the fastest growing economies in the world today have not religiously carried out the so-called Washington consensus and the structural adjustment programs (SAPs) of the World Bank and the IMF. Argentina, on the other hand, a country known to have adopted and implemented both programs, is mired in serious economic crisis and recently announced the suspension of payment of its foreign debt of over $130 billion. Despite their rhetoric the World Bank and the IMF have focused their work in Third World countries on 'mono-economics,' "the view that economics consists of a body of universal truth applicable in all countries and in all conditions" (Singer, 1984, p. 277). It should be noted that a growing number of economists believe the Washington consensus is myopic and misguided. For instance, Stiglitz (1998), a former World Bank economist, claimed the "Washington consensus advocated use of a small set of instruments (including macroeconomic stability, liberalized trade, and privatization) to achieve a relatively narrow goal (economic growth)" (p. 31).

In view of these effects, some critics have claimed that globalization marginalizes Third World countries. Addressing the issue of steadily deteriorating terms of trade of Third World primary commodity producers, Streeten (1981) stated that:

In the world economy there are forces at work that make for an uneven distribution of the gains of trade and economic progress generally, so that the lion's share goes to the lions, while the poor lambs are themselves swallowed up in the process. (p. 217)

The point in all this is that development transcends economic growth, and encompasses other important objectives. We have pursued economic growth in the Third World with great intensity in the hope of solving social problems indirectly through the trickle-down mechanism. This has not happened. In view of their exigencies, social problems merit not merely indirect but direct effort toward their reduction and ultimate elimination. In a 1971 article, the late Mahbub ul Haq, a former Special Adviser to the Administrator of the UNDP and a chief architect of its human development report, argued that:

The problem of development must be defined as a selective attack on the worst forms of poverty. Development goals must be defined in terms of progressive reduction and eventual elimination of malnutrition, disease, illiteracy, squalor, unemployment, and inequalities. We were taught to take care of our GNP and this will take care of poverty. Let use reverse this and take care of poverty as this will take care of the GNP. In other words, let us worry about the content of GNP even more than its rate of increase. (Haq, 1971, p. 11)

This view is in line with development as a human-centered process, which is what Schumacher (1973) meant when he observed:

"Development does not start with goods; it starts with people and their education, organization, and discipline; without these three, all resources remain latent, untapped, potential" (p. 168). People, not passive capital goods and natural resources, are the active agents in the economy of any nation and which are responsible for growing the wealth of nations. As Østergaard (1992) rightly stated,

> People are both the ends and the means of development. Therefore programs of human-resource development must be at the center of economic development strategy. Everything else economic growth, fiscal policy, or exchange-rate management is no more than the means to achieve the fundamental objective of improving human welfare. (p. 1-2)

James D. Wolfensohn, who stepped down as President of the World Bank in May, 2005 acknowledged that "Development thinking has evolved into a broad pragmatism, realizing that development must move beyond economic growth to encompass important social goals--reduced poverty, improved quality of life, enhanced opportunities for better education and health and more" (The World Bank, 2000, p. iii). Nonetheless, the bank and IMF continue to rely rather excessively on getting prices, policies, and institutions "right" in the Third World. This is seen as a necessary action to stimulate growth and reduce divergences in growth among the countries (The World Bank, 2001). May be so, but without specific actions to ensure growth with distribution, one fails to see how this would tackle deteriorating social problems. Apparently, not very much has changed from the earlier approach that was expected to solve problems of poverty, unemployment, and inequality indirectly in the long run.

To assess the progress made in any Third World country, it is no longer sufficient to look exclusively at the rate of expansion of the GDP or at the level of per capita GDP. It has become imperative to address issues concerning poverty, inequality, unemployment, the level of basic needs satisfaction, human capital condition, extent of social discipline and political will, among others. If development meant economic growth alone, most Third World countries performed quite impressively in the 1960s. However Nobel Laureate Gunner Myrdal (1978) wrote that this impressive economic growth took place amidst "increasing maladies such as increased absolute and relative poverty, inequality, unemployment, and wide rural-urban imbalances; and these undesirable accompaniments engendered a genuine desire to give a new meaning to development that would not simply equate it with growth of GNP" (p. 782). It follows then that in assessing a Third World country's development we must ask some specific and pertinent questions. Seers (1973), a critic of Keynes's macroeconomic approach, for instance, suggested asking what he considered the most relevant questions:

> *What has been happening to poverty? What has been happening to unemployment? What has been happening to inequality? If all three of these have declined from high levels, then beyond doubt this has been a period of development for the country concerned. If one or two of these central problems have been growing worse, especially if all three have, it would be strange to call the result "development," even if per capita income doubled.* ((p. 7)

What is Development?

If the reader is getting a sense that development is a complex, multi-dimensional process, you are right. Singer & Ansari (1977) wrote: "A strikingly important aspect of the development process is its complexity; economic, political, social, demographic and cultural factors all interact to produce growth and change" (p. 53). Many have attempted to define development and have been encumbered in doing so by its complexity. No matter how it is defined, it is important to bear in mind that it is human centered. It would suffice here to define human centered development (HCD) simply by paraphrasing Abraham Lincoln's definition of government: HCD is the development of the people, for the people, and by the people. According to Streeten (1995), "Of the people implies adequate income generation through jobs and generation of primary incomes; for the people implies social services for those who need help and the generation of secondary incomes; and by the people means participation" (p. 28). Development is inclusive and more about what people are able to do and be than what goods are produced or preferences satisfied. Development must be seen as an "increasing capacity to make rational use of natural and human resources for social ends" (Mittelman &Pasha, 1997, p. 25). Economic growth and development are related but cannot be used interchangeably because they are not synonymous. Economic growth for sure is vital for development in the Third World, but there is no guarantee that by itself it will deliver development. As was stated before, economic growth is supposed to benefit the poor through the trickle down mechanism, but this is not happening as theorized. Whereas economic growth is concerned with the economy, development concerns changes in a society as a whole, involving social, economic, and political dimensions. Economic growth is a part, a very important part, of development, but the whole is never equal to the sum of its parts or coterminous with a predominant part (Mittelman & Pasha, 1997). Development is multi-faceted and economic growth is one of its facets. A search of the literature for a definition in agreement with this author yielded one by Carley and Christie (1993): "Development is a process by which the members of a society increase their personal and institutional capacities to mobilize and manage resources to produce sustainable and justly distributed improvements in the quality of life consistent with their own aspirations" (p. 41).

Development is not Westernization

In pursuing its diverse objectives, caution must be exercised not to interpret the development of a Third World country as necessarily a process of westernization. The development-as-Westernization mindset is driven by the modernization theory and its "assumption of convergence, that there is one best form of political economy and that all states are moving toward it" (Cullather, 2000, p. 642).

> *Most people are familiar with line convergence in geometry, but not as it relates to global structural transformation. Convergence theory, however, usually assumes that countries with relatively low technological levels will move toward a point already occupied by technologically advanced countries, most of which have been in the orbit of European culture (Japan being the notable exception). Since most advanced technologies have originated in Europe and North America, other countries will have to adopt Western institutions and culture if they are to make effective use of modern technologies. In other words, convergence really means Westernization. (Volti, 2001, p. 268)*

In this mindset, development becomes a process of metamorphosis that transforms a "traditional" Third World society into a city or country that resembles a Western city or country. This is what Liongson (1989) called 'developmentalism,' "a process of economic growth patterned after western countries, that leads to socioeconomic, political, and even cultural dependence" (p. 246). Development, however, does not entail the destruction of valuable national cultures and ethnic traditions of Third World countries. The proclivity to equate development with Westernization explains why we tend to think of it in terms of what we can create, instead of the gradual transformation of society. Schumacher (1973) talked of complexity as the result of evolution, countries being transformed gradually by enlisting the participation of the domestic human resources and selective foreign involvement. In development we cannot assume that what is good for England will be good for Nigeria; just as we cannot assume, as a former GM executive once quipped, that what is good for General Motors is good for America. Development for the Third World is a process of evolution toward self-sufficiency, self-reliance, and less financial, capital, and technological dependence on Western Europe, North America, and Japan. The extent to which development can lead to these objectives depends very much on the quality of domestic human capital. The hope of economic independence in the Third World hinges on good nutrition for good health and the acquisition of appropriate knowledge and skills.

Concluding Remarks

For too long now ideological beliefs and biases have influenced the development discourse and been a major impediment to the realization of the objectives of authentic development in the Third World. Equating development with growth, knowing as most of us do that the whole is greater than the sum of its parts and certainly not coterminous with its dominant part, has not helped matters at all. The theory that wealth will trickle down, on which much of the support for the growth-as-development strategy is based, has not lived up to its promise to reach the poor in general. The great achievements of a number of East Asian countries are testimony that growth, equality, and reductions in poverty can proceed together.

These economies have shown that policies can be formulated that promote growth and equality simultaneously (World Bank, 2000). As noted in UNDP (1997), "Lack of progress in reducing the disadvantages of the deprived cannot be 'wished away' by large advances no matter how large made by the better-off people" (p. 15). The problems of poverty, unemployment, inequality, and limited access to basic needs for increasing number of people cannot be left as it is to the vagaries of "free trade" and international conglomerates to fix. The argument that "something is better than nothing" in the Third World is realistic, but the long-suffering poor cannot wait indefinitely for development to happen in the long run as a by-product of the operations of industrialized-country corporate conglomerates. Going from know-how to know-why in a Third World country will not happen if left to private initiative and multinational corporations alone without the selective and sector-specific government intervention to direct investments (Grieve, 2004). South Korea recognized need to enlist interventionist policies to direct investment in select industries in the economy.

Third World countries are under constant pressure from The World and the International Monetary Fund (IMF) to adopt policies of laissez faire economics, liberalization, and privatization. While the merits of these policies cannot be denied with the right conditions in place, leaving the fate of Third World development to the "invisible hands" of the market alone is not only shortsighted, but foolhardy as well. Privatization, for instance, if undertaken prematurely before a country's entrepreneurial class is developed, during the tenure of a corrupt regime, or forced on a country will do nothing to reduce poverty. In a corrupt regime, privatized enterprises often wind up in the hands of friends, relatives, and/or surrogates of venal regime operatives. Authentic development in the Third World is a desideratum that cannot depend exclusively on the premise of "one size fits all," no matter the strategy in use or under consideration. Both governments and markets must complement each other in the pursuit of development in Third World countries. As most people probably are aware, "markets cannot operate in a vacuum they require a regulatory framework that only governments can provide. The question is not whether the state or market should dominate: each has a unique role to play" (The World Bank, 1991, p. 1). It is wrong to portray government as "an oppressive force, a drag on the economy, and an enemy of private initiative." On the contrary, government is indeed an essential actor in any nation's economy, which plays the role of "a guarantor of fair rules of competition, a countervailing force against excessive private power, a check on the inequalities that capitalism can produce, and an instrument that can open opportunity for those born without great advantages" (Dionne, 2011, p. 4B). A successful development project in Brazil's poverty-stricken northeast involving DaimlerChrysler in 1992 was the result of corporate initiative and pressure from Brazilian and German governments. The pressure from the Green Party in Germany was for then DaimlerBenz to use more renewable natural fibers in its automobiles, and the Brazilian government was demanding that companies with manufacturing plants in the country increase their local content. The outcome was an arrangement initiated by then Daimler Benz in Brazil with a local antipoverty program to construct a modern, high-tech factory that would make headrests and seats out of coconut fibers from locally grown trees (Lodge, 2002).

There is no substitute for the expediency of good governance to spur the socioeconomic development of a country. Governments in the Third World must learn to govern with accountability, transparency, and strict observance of established institutions of governance. Third World leaders must rise above pettiness and develop the political will and social discipline that inspire good governance. Corruption and greed undermine and thwart development efforts and create the propensity to violate human rights and ignore established rules and regulations. A country's socioeconomic problems are not ameliorated when big chunks of

GDP end up in private accounts in foreign banks, or lavished on unproductive projects. Diverting a country's savings or loan monies to acquire jewelry, ostentatious birthday celebrations, or to build palaces will do nothing to alleviate pressing social problems. It is no exaggeration that some members of the ruling class, bureaucrats, and the elite in the Third World have a vested interest in perpetuating poverty. A former German Secretary of development once alleged that he and his counterparts from other developed countries have had to work with the elite of the Third World who were not in the least interested in seeing the poorer classes in the societies advance (Mason, 1997).

Western governments have an important part to play in eradicating corruption and greed in the Third World. Some advanced country governments have a tendency to look the other way while human rights abuses and corrupt practices are perpetuated in the Third World, so long as their interests are being served by a despotic regime. This is a serious source of poverty in the Third World that cannot continue to be ignored. Governments, organizations, and individuals all over the world have a stake in the development of the Third World. I could not agree more with the UNDP (1997) that "Poverty is not to be suffered in silence by the poor; nor can it be tolerated by those with the power to change it" (p. v).

References

Adelman, I. (2001). Fallacies in development theory and their implications for policy. In G. M. Meier & J. E. Stiglitz (Eds.), Frontiers of development economics. The future in perspective (pp. 103-134). New York: Oxford University Press.

Basu, K. (2001). On the goals of development. In G. M. Meier & J. E. Stiglitz (Eds.), Frontiers of development economics. The future in perspective (pp. 61-86). New York: Oxford University Press.

Carley, M. & Christie, I. (1993). *Managing sustainable development.* Minneapolis, MN: University of Minnesota Press.

Cullather, N. (2000). Development? It's history. *Diplomatic History,* 24 (4), 641-53.

Dichenson, I. P., Clarke, C. G., Gould, W. T. S., Prothero, R. M., Siddle, D. J., Smith, C. T., Thomas-Hope, E. M., & Hodgkiss, A. G. (1983). The geography of the Third World. NY: Methuen& Co.

Dionne, E. J. (2011, December 29). Yes, 2012 will set nation's course. St. Cloud Times, p. 4B.

Escobar, A. (1995). Encountering development: The making and unmaking of the Third World. Princeton, NJ: Princeton University Press

Grieve, R, H. (2004). Appropriate technology in a globalizing world. International Journal of Technology Management and Sustainable Development, 3 (3), 173-187.

Haq, M. U. (1971). Employment in the 1970s: A new perspective. *International Development Review*, XIII(4), 9-13.

Higgins, B. & Higgins, J. D. (1979). *Economic development of a small planet*. New York: W. W. Norton & Company, Inc.

Kamrava, M. (2000). Politics and society in the developing world (2nd ed.). NY: Routledge.

Liongson, R. (1989, April/May). Education for development and peace. *Social Education*, pp. 35-36.

Lodge, G. C. (2002). The corporate key: using business to fight global poverty. Foreign Affairs, 81 (4), p.13.

Marglin, ?. (1990).

Mason, M. (1997). *Development and disorder: A history of the Third World since 1945*. Hanover, NH: University Press of New England.

Meier, G. M. (1984). *Emerging from poverty—The economic that really matter*. New York: Oxford University Press.

Meier, G. M. (2001). Introduction: Ideas for development. In G. M. Meier & J. E. Stiglitz (Eds.), *Frontiers of development economics. The future in perspective* (pp. 1-12). New York: Oxford University Press.

Meier, G. M. (2001). The old generation of development economists and the new. In G. M. Meier & J. E. Stiglitz (Eds.), *Frontiers of development economics. The future in perspective* (pp. 13-50). New York: Oxford University Press.

Mittelman, J. H. & Pasha, M. K. (1997). *Out from underdevelopment revisited: Changing global structures and the remaking of the Third World*. New York: St. Martin's Press.

Myrdal, G. (1978, December). Institutional economics. *Journal of Economic Issues, 12*, 771-783.

Ramamurti, R. (2001, Spring). The obsolescing 'bargaining model'? MNC-host developing country relations revisited. (foreign direct investment by multinational corporations) *Journal of International Business Studies, 32*, p. 23.

Rostow, W. W. (1960). *The stages of economic growth: A noncommunist manifesto*. London: Cambridge University Press.

Schumacher, E. F. (1973). *Small is beautiful: Economics as if people mattered*. New York: Harper & Row.

Stiglitz, J. (1998, January 7). More instruments and broader goals: Moving towards the post-Washington consensus. Wider Annual Lecture, Helsinki. Retrieved from the World Wide Web: http://www.worldbank.org/html/extdr/extme/js-010798/wider.htm

Østergaard, L. (1992). Gender. In L. Østergaard (Ed.), Gender and development: A practical guide (pp. 1-10). New York, NY: Routledge.

Singer, H. W. & Ansari, J. A. (1977). *Rich and poor countries.* Baltimore, MD: The Johns Hopkins University Press.

Singer, H. W. (1984). The terms of trade controversy and the evolution of soft financing: Early years in the U.N. In G. M. Meier & Seers, D (Eds.), *Pioneers in development* (pp. 273-311). New York: Oxford University Press.

Streeten, P. (1981). *Development perspectives.* London: Macmillan.

Streeten, P. (1995). Human development: The debate about the index. *International Social Science Journal,* 47(1), 25-37.

Toye, J. (1987). Dilemmas of development: Reflection on the counter-revolution in development theory and policy. NY: Basil Blackwell Inc.

United Nations Development Program (1996). *Human development report, 1996.* New York: Oxford University Press.

United Nations Development Program (1997). *Human development report, 1997.* New York: Oxford University Press.

United Nations Development Program (1999). *Human development report, 1999.* New York: Oxford University Press.

Volti, R. (2001). *Society and Technological change* (4th ed.). New York: Worth Publishers.

Welsh, W. W. & Butorin, P. (Eds.). *Dictionary of development— Third World economy, environment, society (Vols. 1-2).* New York: Garland Publishing Inc.

World Bank (1991). *World development report, 1991*. New York: Oxford University Press.

World Bank (2000). *Entering the 21ˢᵗ century: World development report, 1999/2000*. New York: Oxford University Press.

World Bank (2001). *World development report, 2000/2001*. New York: Oxford University Press.

Young, K. (1993). *Planning development with women: Making a world of difference*. New York: St. Martin's Press.

Chapter FOUR

Basic Needs and Human Development Approaches to Development

Introduction

The recognition that development is a human-centered process and that economic growth alone is an insufficient condition for development engendered the desire for a more inclusive and integrated approach to development. The response to this exigency culminated in programs such as the Basic Needs strategy (BNS) of the International Labor Organization (ILO), the Human Development approach and its accompanying Human Development Index (HDI) initiated by the UNDP, among others. These two initiatives are discussed in this paper.

The Basic Needs Strategy

The basic-needs strategy was introduced in 1976 in an attempt to direct action and resources toward the elimination of poverty, the creation of employment, and the fulfillment of basic needs. Even though a number of Third World countries achieved unprecedented growth during the 1960s, this was described as "growth without development" (Higgins & Higgins, 1979), because it was occurring at the same time with worsening unemployment situation, poverty, and distributional inequity. The disparity in wealth and income was so pronounced that the goal of development could have been that "to those who have something, even more will be given; but those who have nothing, even the little that they have will be taken away from them" (Luke 19: 26, Good News Bible: Luke chapter 19, verse 26, p. 1151). The rich, it appeared, were getting richer and the poor poorer.

The basic-needs strategy was first unveiled at the 1976 World Employment Conference of the ILO in Geneva, Switzerland. Conceptually, the strategy was aimed toward the poor in the Third World as its target group. As envisioned, the basic-needs approach was designed with special emphasis on growth with distribution. As such the primary focus was on basic needs fulfillment rather than the maximization of the national product or income. Basic needs fulfillment means meeting the minimum requirements for a decent life experience within a community. Said differently, basic needs are those needs minimally required to sustain life at a decent material level. They can be categorized as goods and services available to the population. For example, goods include adequate food, clothing, shelter, and adequate household items. Basic services include essentials such as safe drinking water, sanitation, public transportation, and health and educational facilities. A third component of the basic-needs strategy involves a set of basic human rights. These include the rights of citizens to productive employment, decent workplace conditions, and participation in decision-making and project implementation. A key argument of the basic needs approach is that "instead of concentration on maximizing macroeconomic goals (especially growth of production), governments should identify specific unmet needs (nutrition, housing, water, health care, education) and encourage development projects which fulfill some of these" (Hadjor, 1992, p. 47). To pursue this objective, it became paramount in a basic needs strategy to incorporate labor-intensive production methods through investments in socially appropriate technology in the planning and design of these projects as a strategy to promote increasing employment in labor surplus economies. It is claimed that socially appropriate technology is compatible with a basic needs strategy for Third World countries. This is because in "a basic-needs strategy technology must bear the double burden of adapting existing or imported new technology to the general situation of the developing country and of underpinning the redistribution of incomes which goes with a basic-needs strategy" (Carr, 1985, p. 32). Incorporated in a basic-needs strategy, appropriate technology is intended to serve or meet the needs of small farmers, small-scale rural industry, and those of the informal sector operatives in capital-poor economies. The low cost and affordability of appropriate technology, coupled with the constraint imposed by exiguous purchasing power of those targeted in the basic needs strategy explain in part at least this technological preference. Besides, the basic needs strategy is intended to draw the attention of development experts and practitioners back to the true objective of development, which is to provide people in the Third World with the opportunity to realize their full potential. This is well explained in Paul Streeten's articulation of the reasoning underlying the basic needs strategy in Curry (1989):

> Education and health care are required in addition to machines, land, and credit to increase productivity. Sufficient empirical evidence shows that education and health services often make a greater contribution to improving labor productivity than do most alternative investments.

> Many poor people have no physical assets neither a small farm nor a small industry. They are the landless or urban poor. The only asset they possess is their own two hands and their willingness to work. In such a situation, the best investment is in human resource development.

> It is not enough to enable the poor to earn a reasonable income, they also [need goods and services] on which to spend their income. Markets do not always [supply wage goods], and the expansion and redistribution of public services become essential if basic needs of the majority of the population are to be met.

> It may take a long time to increase the productivity of the absolute poor to a level at which they can afford at least the minimum bundle of basic needs for a productive life. In the interim, some income groups particularly in the bottom 10 to 20 percent may need short-term subsidy programs.

> The emphasis on the basic needs, therefore, is a logical step along the path of development thinking. Unfortunately, the term "basic needs" has evoked emotions that have little to do with the meaning that lies behind it. To some, the concept of providing for the basic needs of the poorest represents a futile attempt to redistribute some and provide welfare services to the poor.

> The poor must be fundamentally involved in planning and administering the projects designed to assist them in meeting their needs. (p. 1089)

For all the good intentions of the basic needs strategy, its implementation was undermined by perceptions about its timing. Part of the skepticism of the basic needs critics was directed toward the perceived motive behind the program. The special promotional effort to establish the basic needs strategy in the 1970s was interpreted correctly or incorrectly as a scheme by international development agencies in collaboration with the industrialized countries to keep the third World in its place (UNDP, 1996). The scheme was seen as an attempt to divert attention away from the inequities within the global economic system and the widening socioeconomic gap between the rich and poor nations. Particularly, pushing a basic needs strategy almost immediately following the abortive call for a new international economic order (NIEO) was seen as a surreptitious attempt to circumvent an issue of paramount importance to the Third World (Welsh & Butorin, 1990). Critics also alleged the pervasion of the original intent of the basic needs strategy by governments and agencies. Instead of empowering the poor economically and ensuring their active participation in decision-making and project implementation, the basic needs strategy was turned into top-down state initiatives that simply "count the poor, cost the bundle, and deliver to them" (UNDP, 1996, p. 48). The launching of the basic needs strategy so close to the 1980s when the debt crisis first appeared as a matter of serious international concern did not help matters at all. Under pressure to service their debt and implement the structural adjustment programs (SAPs) of the IMF, many Third World countries were forced to cut many basic needs programs. According to Oxfam International, a decade of SAPs reversed hard-won gains in health and education, caused a decline in living standards, and aggravated poverty especially in Sub-Saharan Africa (Moyo, 1993). Uganda is often cited as an example of a country that spent $3 on health per citizen each year, and a mind-boggling $7 a person on debt repayment to mostly multilateral lenders such as the World Bank and the IMF (Lewis, 1996). Despite these weaknesses, the basic needs strategy played the important role of refocusing attention on the central purpose of development; that is, human-centered development. As we shall see in the next section, some of the authors of the basic needs strategy also collaborated with the United Nations Development Program (UNDP) to initiate the human development approach in 1990.

The Human Development Approach

Although of minimal success due partially to the above problems, the basic needs strategy has maintained relevance as a people-centered strategy concerned with human development. Streeten (1995) even referred to human development as "an extension, enlargement and deepening of the now somewhat unpopular basic needs approach" (p. 25). The major difference between the two approaches is mainly in their scope and the economic status of the target group. While the basic needs strategy targeted the poor in the Third World, the human development program is broader in scope, including all human beings regardless of their location and economic status. Anand and Ravallion (1993) remarked that the human development approach to development "relates to earlier works on basic needs...though the focus is more integrated and less ad hoc in the concept of 'human development'" (p. 133). The appeals of human development can hardly be overstated. In a summarized rendition of Paul Streeten's reasons why all should be interested in human development Basu (2001) wrote:

> *Human development is desirable as an end in itself. It can promote higher productivity and so enhance human command over goods and services. It reduces human reproduction, an outcome that is generally considered desirable. It is good for the environment. It can contribute to a healthy civil society and democracy. It can promote political stability. (p. 65)*

Human development, as defined in the first annual human development report (HDR) published in 1990 is "both the process of widening people's choices and the level of achieved well being" (UNDP, 1990, p. 9). One message presented repeatedly in the annual reports is that economic development is not by itself tantamount to human development. The issues commonly discussed in the reports are, for instance, whether a government cares more about economic development alone or about health care and education as well; whether it spends the money it controls more on armaments or on teachers; whether women are just toilers in the field or share in the wealth and responsibilities of a nation (Genovese, 1990). Human development seeks, among other things, the fulfillment of people's desires to lead a long and healthy life, to acquire knowledge, and to have access to the resources needed for a decent standard of living. The two sides to human development, "the formation of human capabilities such as improved health, knowledge, and skills and the use people make of their acquired capabilities for leisure, productive purposes or being active in cultural, social and political affairs" (UNDP, 1990, p. 10), are emphasized in recognition and pursuit of these human desires. The human development index (HDI) established to go with the human development approach is an aggregate of three indicators composed of these afore-mentioned human goals.

The Human Development Index

Since the end of World War II, per capita income or GDP has been the dominant development index. There is little doubt that per capita GDP is effective as an indicator of a country's macroeconomic performance, but is hardly adequate as a measure of the level of the well-being or welfare of that country's residents. Serafy (1995) observed, "Per capita income estimates that overlook income distribution and the incidence of poverty, and aggregates that neglect the erosion of the environment, are poor guides to developmental change" (p. 71). Critics have consistently faulted per capita income for its silence on distributional inequities, environmental plundering and degradation, rapid depletion of nonrenewable resources, and diminishing biodiversity. The attraction and dominance of per capita GDP as a development index can be attributed to a number of factors. First, it is simple, using only quantifiable items, and therefore appealing to many governments, economists, and the media; second, there is so far no single indicator of comparably superior quality to replace it; and, last but not least, it serves the interest of the industrial North who naturally want to maintain the status quo. Another possible explanation for the staying power of average income is the inertia of "we-have-always-done-it-that-way" syndrome. However, Sachs (1995) made a rather compelling point when he asked somewhat rhetorically, "Do we have to be confined solely to measurement in the strict sense on the grounds that anything that cannot be quantified is irrelevant, or, on the contrary, give preference to the qualitative approach?" (p. 6).

Recognizing the shortcomings of per capita income as a measure of human well being, the UNDP developed the human development index (HDI) as a complementary index. The HDI itself is a variation of the Physical Quality of Life Index (PQLI) a non-income based indicator that emerged from the 1979 collaborative effort of Morris David Morris and the Overseas Development Council (ODC) (Gonzalez, 1988). Based on a measuring scale of 0 to 1.0, the HDI is an aggregate of three indices, namely, longevity, knowledge, and command over resources needed for a decent living standard. Longevity is measured by life expectancy at birth, knowledge by literacy, because reading is the source of information and understanding; and the command over resources by real per capita income adjusted for purchasing power (Brown et al, 1991; UN Chronicle, 1990). The UN Chronicle (1990) noted that the HDI "illustrates how economic growth and wealth alone do not necessarily translate into greater human development for the majority of the people" (p. 49). It is possible for a country with a high per capita income to have relatively exiguous improvements in the lives of its citizens, and for a country with an unimpressive average income to have greatly improved living conditions for a majority of its citizens. In other words, poverty may be wide spread in a country with a high per capita income (PCI) and low HDI, and not as bad in a country with a high HDI and low PCI. The difference in both instances has to do with the pattern of income distribution and the extent people have access to essential resources and services in each country. Like per capita income, the HDI is made up of national averages that do not deal directly with distributional inequity; but by including longevity and literacy they do indirectly reflect the distribution of resources. A comparison of two Third World countries, South Africa and Sri Lanka, will illustrate this point. South Africa has a PCI of $8,908 and an HDI of 0.702, and Sri Lanka a PCI of $3,279 and an HDI of 0.735. Although South Africa has a PCI more than two times that of Sri Lanka, it has a lower HDI than Sri Lanka (UNDP, 2001). This is because wealth is more evenly distributed in Sri Lanka, along with access to food and social services, whereas in South Africa it is largely concentrated in the hands of a few wealthy individuals. The high average life expectancy of 71.9 years in Sri Lanka, for instance, indicates broad access to health care and to adequate supplies of food (UNDP, 2001; Brown et al, 1991).

The HDI, as is true of most existing development indices, is not a panacea and has been criticized for some flaws here and there. One concern that has been expressed is that improvements in life expectancy, literacy, or purchasing power could be "financed by the depletion of natural support systems, setting the stage for a long-term deterioration in living conditions" (Brown et al, 1991, p. 10). This is to say that the HDI, just like per capita GDP, does not deal at least directly with issues of environmental concern; and given today's priorities and sensitivity to the environment, this is a very serious oversight. However, other more widely held criticisms of the HDI, such as claims of its arbitrariness and questionable international comparability, have been made (Lipton, 2001; Srinivasan, 1994). A rather blunt criticism in this regard came from Srinivasan (1994):

The HDI is conceptually weak and empirically unsound, involving serious problems of comparability over time and space, measurement errors, and biases. Meaningful inferences about the process of development and performance as well as policy implications could hardly be drawn from variations in HDI. (p. 241)

Lipton (2001) added,

It is bad enough that economists add up planes, trains, and violin concertos into GDP. However, unlike the HDI, GDP is an aggregation for which there are (a) good reasons, (b) testable, micro-founded theories of the causes of change and of the tradeoffs, positive or negative, between such change and other desiderata, and (c) accessible measures of how components should be weighted (that is, by relative prices). (p. 96)

It is a common tendency in the development field to be exclusive rather than inclusive about ideas. Lipton (2001) lauded the HDI and its variants as "an alternative ladder that GDP-index-fixated politicians might climb to see the problems of health, literacy, gender, and poverty reduction" (p. 96). While believing that the HDI and its variants perform important services, Lipton (2001) argued at the same time that the "ladder" was flawed and should be thrown away. An interesting irony in the development discourse is that we readily see and acknowledge the imperfections and merits of methods or strategies but vehemently argue against using two or more indices of development that complement each other for better and realistic results. This inclination only shows our predisposition to do things the same way they have always been done regardless of changing circumstances and the differences in time and space. This is we-have-always-done-it-this-way syndrome mentioned earlier, which has plagued the discipline for too long and has been perhaps an insuperable barrier to development. It is hard not to recognize the distraction this has become, drawing attention away from the real issues of development. Instead of dealing with poverty, unemployment, inequality, and basic needs fulfillment, we are preoccupied with personal politics and engaged in ideological conundrums, while people around the world suffer needlessly in squalid poverty. The resounding message of the 1997 Human Development Report is that "poverty is no longer inevitable and that the world has the material and natural resources; the know-how; and the people to make a poverty-free world a reality in less than a generation" (UNDP, 1997, p. iii). As James Gustav Speth, a former UNDP Administrator, pointed out, "this is not woolly idealism but a practical and achievable goal" (UNDP, 1997, p. iii). Perhaps the attention of HDI critics and votaries of per capita GDP should be drawn to a statement in the 1993 HDR and similar ones elsewhere that "The HDI should be seen as evolving and improving rather than as something cast in stone" (UNDP, 1993, 104). Recognizing the imperfection of the HDI, the UNDP has consistently developed new supplementary indicators. For example, the 1995 HDR featured two new indices: gender-related development index (GDI) and the gender empowerment measure (GEM). The GDI is an adjusted version of the HDI and deals with gender inequality. "In other words, if a nation's women are doing worse than its men in earnings, education, or life expectancy, the country will have a lower GDI than HDI" (Forcione & Breslow, 1995, p. 43). "The GEM measures gender inequality in economic and political opportunities" (UNDP, 2000, p. 147), and is calculated with three factors that are weighted equally: women's job status, political status, and income status (Forcione & Breslow, 1995). Other indices, such as the human poverty index introduced in the 1997 HDR, have since been added.

References

Anand, S. & Ravallion, M. (1993). Human development in poor countries: On the role of private incomes and public services. Journal of Economic Perspectives, 7 (1), 133-149.

Basu, K. (2001). On the goals of development. In G. M. Meier & J. E. Stiglitz (Eds.), Frontiers of development economics. The future in perspective (pp. 61-86). New York: Oxford University Press.

Brown, L. R. (1991). The new world order. In L. R. Brown et al, State of the world, 1991 (pp. 3-20). New York: W. W. Norton and Company.

Curry, Jr., R. L. (1989). The basic needs strategy, the Congressional mandate, and U. S. foreign aid policy. The Journal of Economic Issues, XXIII (4), 1085-1096.

Forcione, C. & Breslow, M. (1995, November-December). Measuring women's progress. Dollars and Sense, 202, 43.

Higgins, B. & Higgins, J. D. (1979). *Economic development of a small planet.* New York: W. W. Norton & Company, Inc.

Sachs, I. (1995). The quantitative and qualitative measurement of development: Its implications and limitations. International Social Science Journal, 47 (1), 1-9.

Serafy, S. E. (1995). Measuring development: the role of environmental accounting. International Social Science Journal, 47 (1), 61-72.

Singer, H. W. (1985). Appropriate technology and basic-needs strategy. In M. Carr (Ed.), The AT reader: Theory and practice in appropriate technology (pp. 32-33). Croton-on-Hudson, NY: Intermediate Technology Development Group of North America.

Streeten, P. (1995). Human development: The debate about the index. *International Social Science Journal*, 47(1), 25-37.

United Nations Development Program (1990). *Human development report, 1990*. New York: Oxford University Press.

United Nations Development Program (1993). *Human development report, 1993*. New York: Oxford University Press.

United Nations Development Program (1996). *Human development report, 1996*. New York: Oxford University Press.

United Nations Development Program (1997). *Human development report, 1997*. New York: Oxford University Press.

United Nations Development Program (1999). *Human development report, 1999*. New York: Oxford University Press.

United Nations Development Program (2000). *Human development report, 2000*. New York: Oxford University Press.

Welsh, W. W. & Butorin, P. (Eds.). *Dictionary of development—Third World economy, environment, society (Vols.* 1-2). New York: Garland Publishing Inc.

World Bank (1991). *World development report, 1991*. New York: Oxford University Press.

World Bank (2000). *Entering the 21st century: World development report, 1999/2000*. New York: Oxford University Press.

World Bank (2001). *World development report, 2000/2001*. New York: Oxford University Press.

Young, K. (1993). *Planning development with women: Making a world of difference*. New York: St. Martin's Press.

Chapter FIVE

Technology and Technology Transfer for Third World Development

Introduction

The application of technology to stimulate development in the Third World received unqualified endorsement and support after World War II. In the postwar period from the late 1940s through the early 1960s in particular, a great number of former European colonies in Africa and Asia emerged from the bonds of colonialism to become independent countries. The acquisition and application of technology was considered integral to accelerated development in the newly independent nations. From a classical economic standpoint, development was synonymous with economic growth and industrialization was essential to that growth. Thus, to industrialize, capital accumulation, infrastructure development, foreign technical experts, and the importation of modern technology from the industrialized world were deemed indispensable. Each newly independent country opted for a strategy of industrialization deemed appropriate for its national development goals. Dependent on those goals, a country adopted either an import-substitution industrialization (ISI) (to enable the country to manufacture goods that were previously imported for domestic consumption), an export-oriented industrialization (EOI) (to enable the country to manufacture goods for export to other countries), or a combination of both. Regardless of the strategy adopted, implementation invariably required the importation of capital goods (that is, machines, equipment, and plants) and the development of national infrastructure for domestic production of manufactured goods. The importation of technology or the so-called transfer of technology from the rich to the new nations that ensued, especially from the mid-1960s, was intended to spur development through industrialization. Thus the development of the Third World for all intents and purposes was linked with the acquisition and utilization of technology from advanced Western countries.

Decades of technology transfer have not produced the expected outcome, considering the dismal social and economic conditions in many Third World countries today. The anticipated transformation in the economies of Third World countries has, so far, been elusive. What went wrong? Why has the outcome of technology transfer to the Third World been so disappointing? What is technology? What is technology transfer? Is technology transfer to the Third World what it should be? Under what conditions can the transfer of technology stimulate innovation and development in the Third World?

The purpose of this chapter is to discuss the issues raised in these questions concerning technology and its transfer to the Third World. Specifically, the chapter discusses the current practice of technology transfer and how it can be made more effective in stimulating development in the Third World. Given this objective, it makes good sense to begin with a discussion of the meaning of technology. It is difficult to dispute the point Volti (2001) made that "gaining an understanding of the meaning of words is often the beginning of knowledge" (p.4). To this end, the chapter will begin with a discussion of the concept of technology in an attempt to provide some background information and common definitions for the discussion later on the transfer of technology to Third World countries.

About Technology

Technology is a relatively recent word. In 1831 Professor Jacob Bigelow of Harvard University published *Elements of Technology*, the first book published in English, as far as we know, with the word *technology* in the title (Volti, 2001). However, the etymological roots of the word can be traced beyond the 1800s to the Greek. Research reveals that *technology* was invented by combining the root word *techne* or *techno*, which denotes that having to do with the technical aspects of the arts and crafts, with the suffix word *logia* or *logos*, which denotes theory, doctrine, science, or the study of (Wiens and Wiens, 1996). Technology is defined the book as: "the principles, processes, and nomenclatures of the more conspicuous arts, particularly those which involve applications of science" (Volti, 2001, p.4). This initial definition certainly provided invaluable foundational insights into the sense of the word as a concept. While gaining a sense of how a word was used in the past certainly enhances our present knowledge and understanding of the word, it is also true that the meaning of technology has evolved etymologically since Professor Bigelow used it.

Technology entails, but is not synonymous with, machines, equipment, plants, tools, or instruments. These technical devices embody technology, but technology also exists as knowledge, techniques, skills, ideas, and organization, which are people-bound in character. Thus we can speak of the material and nonmaterial nature of technology. Technology is multidimensional and, as a result, cannot be defined with precision or consistency (Willoughby, 1990). That said; it is also true that our knowledge and understanding of concepts tend to be better informed when they are discussed from various perspectives. Some definitions of technology begin by stating that it is a system, others with a process or the study of something. However, what most definitions appear to have in common is they tend to delineate the material and nonmaterial character of technology. Sharif (1992), for example, defines it as "a complex combination of continuously improved physical assets, progressively learned skills, routinely acquired knowledge, and evolving management practices" (p. 391). Volti (2001) defines technology as "a system based on the application of knowledge, manifested in physical objects and organizational forms, for the attainment of specific goals" (p. 6). Pytlik, Lauda, & Johnson (1985) define technology as the study of the technical means undertaken in all cultures, which involves the systematic application of organized knowledge and tangibles for the extension of human faculties..." (p. 5). From this author's perspective, technology refers to an intellectually based human process that gives rise to the synthesis and accumulation of knowledge from which skills, ideas, processes, techniques, technical devices, and more knowledge are generated to augment human capacity to solve practical problems. The material part of technology, which includes capital goods and others, can be exchanged easily through sales to the highest bidder. On the other hand, knowledge, ideas, techniques, organization, and skills--the nonmaterial aspect of technology--cannot be transferred directly due to their person-bound character. As will be shown next, this distinction is crucial in judging whether a transfer of technology is, or is not, successful.

Technology Transfer to the Third World

Perceptions and assumptions about technology can and do affect the outcome of its transfer. A popular perception of technology is that it comprises physical objects mentioned earlier. The problem with equating technology with physical objects only is that so much is often assumed away. It is often assumed that if a machine or a "technique of production" works perfectly well in the country and circumstances in which it was created and nurtured, it should do just fine in any other locale. First, technology does not function in a social vacuum as this line of reasoning seems to suggest, it depends on factors such as the prevailing social relations, physical as well as human infrastructure, and raw material availability. Technology is like genetic material that will produce the anticipated result only when all the necessary factors or inputs are present. Secondly, the suggestion that the transfer of technology provides all that Third World countries need for technological, social, and economic development when these countries receive capital goods or techniques of production from the industrialized world is false and misleading. It is false, because several of the elements implied have no basis in reality. For instance, it is not true that Third World countries have no problem absorbing transferred technologies; that adaptations are not required; that all companies remain equally efficient; and that firm-specific learning or technical effort is unnecessary and irrelevant (Lall, 1992; Diwan and Livingston, 1979).

As mentioned earlier, capital goods embody, but do not by themselves constitute technology; they are product, object-embodied, or material-type technologies that can be purchased freely on the international market. A transfer involving object-embodied technology is referred to as *material transfer*. If the import of such technical means were all that was necessary, many Third World countries would be as industrialized today as their counterparts in Europe and North America. Saudi Arabia can be used to illustrate this point. With all its oil wealth and billions of dollars in foreign reserves, Saudi Arabia is able to buy sophisticated machines and equipment from Europe, North America, and Japan; however, the country's telephone system, for instance, remains comparatively second-rate. The transfer of technology entails much more than the mere acquisition of physical assets. The purchase of a house, for instance, does not constitute a transfer of the architectural and construction knowledge and skill that went into its establishment. The technology transfer process is more like learning carpentry than purchasing a new drill. "If one does not develop the skill to use the tool adeptly, and if one does not understand how one particular stage relates to other stages of production, one's product will be inferior and not sell" (Mittelman and Pasha, 1997, p.61). By the same token, the purchase and possession of a machine or equipment by a Third World country neither bestows upon the people of the country the scientific and technological knowledge essential to its production locally, nor the ability to set it up a plant for efficient production. In fact, it is the contention of some scholars in the field that material-transfer is not actually a form of "technology" transfer. According to this school of thought, the important ingredient in material-transfer "is not 'know-how' but 'show-how' and the core technologies are embodied within the physical items" (Simon, 1991, p. 8). In other words, in material transfer the recipient is able to consume the artifact but does not develop the ability to reproduce the knowledge. Emmanuel (1982), an adherent of this school of thought, argued similarly that the export of a machine "rather constitutes a substitute for the transfer of the technology which would have been necessary in order to produce it locally, and is a sort of non-transfer" (p. 22). This point underlies the statement by Jequier (1976) on the importation of objected-embodied technologies.

> The symbols of modernity, in the form of steel mills, chemical plants, automobile factories or squadrons of military aircrafts can be purchased on the international market, but development is a complex social process, which rests in large part upon the internal innovative capabilities of a society. Imports of foreign ideas, values and technologies have a major part to play, but few societies in history have developed exclusively on the basis of such imports. (p. 16)

However, most models of technology transfer are usually based on ideal conditions in which transactions involve equally endowed senders and receivers of technology. In other words, there is no difference whatsoever between senders and receivers of technology. Thus, Third World countries are taken to possess the capacity to integrate imported technology into production processes on their own without needing assistance. As Stolp (1993) pointed out, "this perspective places the recipient and its capacity to absorb new technology on an equal conceptual footing with Northern senders of technology" (p.156). However, this is certainly not the case. Whereas the transfer of technology involving two firms from two technologically advanced countries often results in mutual benefits and technological interdependence between the participants, the same cannot always be said about transactions involving industrialized and Third World countries. A strategic alliance involving Motorola of the United States and Toshiba of Japan illustrates this point. In this alliance, Motorola exchanged its microprocessor technology with Toshiba for the latter's memory technology. In addition, Toshiba also agreed to assist Motorola in expanding its sales into the Japanese electronics market (Simon, 1991). This is typical in most strategic alliances, where the critical and determining factor is the existence of balance in the benefits that each firm derives from the transaction or alliance. That the transfer of technology between two firms from industrialized countries is mutually beneficial to the firms can be attributed to their superior scientific and technological knowledge, which constitute the basis for the development of capital goods and related physical structures. The successful economic recovery of both Europe and Japan after World War II, with the help of the United States' Marshall Plan, is another event that illustrates this point. Those who equate technology with physical structures believe that the fast recovery of Europe and Japan was an "economic miracle." The truth is that physical structures constitute only the visible character of technology or metaphorically a tip of the iceberg. The submerged base of the iceberg or the invisible aspect of technology knowledge, skills, and organization---remained intact after the physical industrial structures were smashed to pieces during World War II (Schumacher, 1973). It was this invisible form of technology, of which people are the carriers, which enabled the countries to rebuild their economies as rapidly as they did after the war. Europe and Japan possess an absorptive capacity lacking in most Third World countries, and were able to rebuild once they received Marshall Aid funds (Aharoni, 1991).

Technology "transfer connotes the movement of knowledge, skill, organization, values and capital from the point of generation to the site of adaptation and application" (Mittelman and Pasha, 1997, p.60). It is the useful exchange of ideas and innovations in such a way that allows the receiving region or country to expand on and utilize the knowledge received. A critical test of technology transfers, therefore, is whether they stimulate further innovations within the recipient country. For instance, the transmission of information about the invention of gunpowder and some basic gun-like devices in China stimulated the invention of the formidable cannon in Europe. Information about transistor technology from the United States provoked the development of new kinds of consumer products in Japan (Pacey, 1990). This is not happening in Third World countries to the extent expected despite decades of massive importation of object-embodied technologies from the industrialized world. The intent here is not to imply that capital goods are not important. On the contrary, investment in capital assets is an indispensable prerequisite of economic growth. However, the primacy of people as the ultimate basis for the wealth of a nation is indisputable. As the active participants in any economy, human beings accumulate capital, exploit natural resources, build social, economic, and political organizations, and affect national development. Capital and natural resources, on the other hand, are passive factors of production that depend on human manipulation to be useful. As Meier (1984) aptly observed, "Clearly, a country which is unable to develop the skills and knowledge of its people and utilize them effectively in the national economy will be unable to develop anything else" (p.3).

The point is that many Third World countries are not developing the human as well as the physical capital that they need to build and enhance their national stock of capital. Domestic capital development and investment is essential to a country's income generating capacity. Foreign ownership of capital has served foreign investors well, enabling them to repatriate large amounts of income or profit abroad at the expense of the host Third World countries. Aggarwal (1991) identified the direct or first order costs associated with the disadvantages of technology transfer to Third World countries by the transferring firm to include the "outflow of dividends, profits, management and royalty fees, interest on loans, and other remittances by the firm including the possible use of high transfer prices" (p. 69). Technology transfer as we know it has not brought domestic expansion of innovations or done much to promote indigenous human as well as material capital development in most Third World countries. When a country cannot on its own exploit imported technology to improve domestic production, let alone learn from it to further domestic innovation, it is inappropriate to speak of a transfer of technology taking place. The capacity to assimilate, adapt, modify, and/or generate technology is critical to an effective transfer of technology. For this to happen, Pellegrini (1980) remarked that "transfer must be strictly correlated to the acquisition of the know-how by community's people themselves that have to participate in the shaping of the technical economic and social change" (p. 5). Rosenberg (1972) made the same point when he wrote:

> *New techniques frequently require considerable modification before they can function successfully in a new environment. This process of modification often involves a higher order of skill and ability, which is typically underestimated or ignored. Yet, the capacity to*

achieve these modifications and adaptations is critical to the successful transfer of technology a transfer which is too frequently thought of as merely a matter of transporting a piece of hardware from one location to another. (Rosenberg, 1972, pp. 61-62)

Material transfer, as noted earlier, involves 'show-how,' but not 'know-how;' the recipient of material transfer can consume/use the technology, but does not develop the ability to reproduce the knowledge/technology. A second class of technology transfer, known as *design transfer*, provides the recipient with designs, formulas, patents, documents, technical data, blueprints and know-how to manufacture previously designed products or equipment. Design transfer is an improvement over material transfer in the sense that it builds capability where the recipient firm or country can produce the machines or the products, although the country or firm will remain dependent on the foreign supplier for any changes in design (Aharoni, 1991). The class of technology transfer that leads to self-reliance and self-sustained growth of the recipient country or firm is known as *capacity-transfer*. It is often referred to as the *active transfer*, because capacity transfer allows the recipient to reproduce the knowledge and change it, adapting it to different conditions (Aharoni, 1991). Capacity transfer enables Third World countries to take advantage of the preponderant power of technology as an effective means of fostering sustainable socioeconomic development. Capacity transfer develops the human capital and technological capability of the recipient Third World country or firm. Grieve (2004) noted that "creating technological capability is not merely about acquiring and installing new machinery. It involves also the development of human resources. Decision-makers may first have to 'learn how to learn' if industry in a developing country is ever to succeed in assimilating a new technological culture" (p. 180).

Technological capability is the same idea the United Nations called "indigenous technological capability" (ITC), which has to do with the knowledge and skills of a country's human capital, and other absorptive elements such as infrastructure, raw materials, and such things as the nature of the soil and climate. Among the attributes of a society that has acquired ITC are: an understanding of its technological needs; an effective policy on technology and its acquisition; effective global scanning and search procedures for identifying and selecting the most beneficial technology and supplier; the ability to evaluate the appropriateness of the technology to be imported; a strong bargaining or negotiating expertise needed for technological acquisitions; technical and organizational skills to use imported technology; the ability to adapt imported technology to local conditions; the availability of requisite infrastructure and raw materials; and the capacity to solve its problem using its resources. According to the United Nations (1983) ITC is not an alternative to a successful technology transfer but a necessary condition for it. The difficulty that most Third World countries face in trying to build their ITC can be blamed on internal as well as external obstacles.

Obstacles to Building Indigenous Technological Capability (ITC)

Third World countries have relied heavily on industrialized world sources for the acquisition of technical knowledge and skills. Those involved in the export of technology from industrialized countries are individual entrepreneurs, non-governmental organizations (NGOs), government agencies, multilateral agencies, religious organizations, foundations, universities, consulting firms, and of course multinational corporations (MNCs). In terms of the degree of involvement, MNCs, described as the most prolific purveyors of technology transfer (Simon, 1991), are by far the dominant group. They own and operate multibillion-dollar research and development facilities for generating new knowledge and innovations. The resulting knowledge and innovations are protected under lock and key within the confines of the MNCs. The extent to which MNCs transfer or provide technological knowledge and innovations to Third World countries remains open to debate. It is no exaggeration that the vaunted transmission of technological knowledge and innovations by MNCs often is a carefully monitored flow from corporate headquarters to the premises of a subsidiary in the Third World (Mittelman and Pasha, 1997). In fact, the activities of most MNCs may be described as guided primarily by the profit motive. It does not come as a surprise to anyone that MNCs do not operate with the objective to intentionally transfer innovative capacity to the Third World. In fact, Mittelman and Pasha (1997) wrote that "the transfer of technology, to the extent that it actually occurs, is nothing other than leakage from [M] NCs" (p.63). In other words, MNCs are not into *capacity-transfers*. Ironically, capacity transfers are the most coveted category of technology transfer that lead to the development of indigenous technological capability and absorptive capacity in host Third World countries. It is, however, naïve to expect that all MNCs will readily work to build the technological capability and self-reliance of countries that constitute a very significant source of corporate profits.

Similarly, bilateral and multilateral assistance to Third World countries, is not, as most people would believe, an act of charity. It has been said that aid actually inhibits forms of development that do not suit the donor (Mason, 1997). This statement cannot be entirely false, especially knowing that government-to-government assistance without expecting something in return goes against the fundamental law of economics that "there is no free lunch." Foreign aid, comprising "money and technology or technique aimed ostensibly at encouraging or supporting development; money for arms and training; and money and goods for health and emergency relief" (Mason, 1997, p.432), was intended to accomplish two major purposes:

to ensure that the economies of the Third World functioned efficiently, because the prosperity of the West was closely connected to the purchasing power and raw materials of the non-West; and, just as in Europe, to discourage the development of national capitalism or communism in any form. (Mason, 1997, p.433)

This is not an attempt to diminish the value of foreign aid. The point, however, is that foreign aid seldom happens without strings attached. It is hardly a secret that foreign aid has helped create foreign appetite in the Third World. Not too long after World War II, most Third World countries could feed themselves, but that is hardly the case anymore. Mason (1997) noted, for instance, that "As a result of U.S. food aid policies, recipient countries were forced to modify both their own food policies and the eating habits of their people" (p. 431). The beneficiaries of this turn of events are most U.S.-based multinational agribusinesses, United States farmers, and consumers. It is no wonder in most Third World societies that "local peoples largely produce what they do not consume and consume what they do not produce" (Mittelman and Pasha, 1997, p. 47). Thanks to sophisticated communications and transportation technologies, the Third World is no longer shielded from the global wind of change ushering in what Mason (1997) termed "'McWorld,' a gustatory metaphor for globalization" (p. 408).

However, the impediments to technological development in the Third World are not all externally induced. Reluctance on the part of Third World elite to undertake the educational and technological effort needed to gain mastery over technology is also a part of the problem. Believing the acquisition of machines and other technical devices to be their priority, Third World countries embarked on a massive but passive importation of technology. Today, the landscape of most Third World countries is littered with expensive machines and construction equipment that are rusting away due to scarcity of spare parts and lack of maintenance. Literary educational curriculum inherited from past colonial administrations has not been changed or adapted to address the technological and socioeconomic needs of most Third World countries. Technical, technology, and vocational education are regarded to be less in importance relative to literary education. In fact, graduates of technical and vocational education are often looked down upon as individuals without enough brainpower or mental aptitude for literary education, who are, therefore, routed to the less prestigious technical schools. In other words, they are rejects of literary education (Akubue, 1991). The ambition of most Third World youth to work in air-conditioned offices just like the former colonial administrators, themselves graduates of literary education, reminds one of what Diwan and Livingston (1979) described as the "assimilative effect of colonialism." Until they see fit to develop educational systems that address their particular needs and develop a sense of their true priorities, Third World countries will continue to lack the absorptive capacity to utilize technology to foster their development and raise the general standard of living. This is a point that is supported by the many years these countries have tried to take advantage of different mechanisms of technology transfer to no avail. Mechanisms of technology transfer are vast and varied, including direct foreign investments, joint ventures, licensing, training, commercial visits, print literature, the internet, sales of products, turnkey projects, and so on. Some of these are discussed in the next section.

Mechanisms for Technology Transfer

Due to the constraint of space only four of the major modes of technology transfer are discussed here; namely, direct foreign investments, joint ventures, licensing, and turnkey projects.

Foreign Direct Investment

Foreign direct investment (FDI) is one of the more frequently used channels of technology transfer. An FDI is usually a long-term productive investment in foreign countries in which an investing multinational corporation exercises either full or partial management control of assets and production in the countries involved (Siddiqi, 2001; Mallampally and Sauvant, 1999). To attract FDIs, Third World countries are promising policy liberalization, political stability, privatization, and minimal government intervention. Where all or a portion of these conditions are assured, a foreign corporation may be motivated to set up production facilities in a Third World country. Among other things, multinational corporations invest in the Third World to protect an existing market or to create a new one, to bypass prohibitive barriers and import restrictions, to discover or protect raw material sources, to renew product's life cycle, to take advantage of cheap labor and skills, and to increase profits (Kaynak, 1985). Opinions differ as to the benefits of FDI to the Third World. While some argue that benefits include transfers of production technology, managerial expertise, skills, innovative capacity, and increasing access to global markets, others are less convinced and argue that any transfers to the Third World as a result of FDIs are mainly unintended leakage (Mittelman and Pasha, 1997). Whatever the argument, it is doubtful, from decades of experience, that FDIs are a significant source of capacity building and national capital formation in host Third World countries. Writing somewhat apologetically on foreign investment in the Third World Nurkse (1960) noted that:

> *Naturally it does not always pay foreign-owned business enterprise to invest in the education and technical training of local labor, especially if any labor so trained is not tied to that firm and can at any time go to another employer. (pp. 88-89)*

In any case, FDIs are once more in high demand after the setback in the 1970s when a number of Third World governments nationalized many foreign firms after accusing them of exploitation and excessive profit repatriation. It has to be pointed out, however, that as many Third World countries improve their bargaining power and the ability to absorb foreign technology, their quest for equity in contract negotiations with foreign multination corporations has been growing. One of the consequences of this development is a growing interest in establishing joint ventures between multinational corporations and host Third World country governments or enterprises. According to Goulet (1989), "Pressured by new demands from governments, many TNCs which have favored direct foreign investments only when they could be sole owners of enterprises are now agreeing to become minority equity holders in joint ventures.

Joint Ventures

Joint ventures have become attractive as many MNCs seek to take advantage of similar benefits as in FDIs, but at the same time avoid the risk of nationalization that may be potentially high with FDIs. Broadly, a joint venture may be defined as "a partnership formed by a company in one country with a company in another country for the purpose of pursuing some mutually desirable business undertaking" (Certo, 1986, p. 521). In strategic alliances such as this, ownership is based on equity share. The partners in the alliance each provide a portion of the equity or the equivalent in physical plant, raw materials, cash, or other assets (Griffin, 1990). In some Third World countries, MNCs are limited in equity ownership to fifty percent or less. Even then, joint ventures are attractive to MNCs for reasons that are both tangible and intangible. First, the Third World private or government partner may contribute land, funding, as well as vital knowledge of domestic markets, suppliers, and patterns of business practice (Kaynak, 1985). The alliance combines the technical expertise the MNC with the understanding that the host-country partner has regarding how to circumvent or eliminate government red tape that may affect the operations of the firm. In addition, joint ventures offer a number of intangible advantages, such as creating goodwill with Third World governments, employees, customers, as well as reduced risk of nationalization or unfavorable government legislation (Kaynak, 1985). In a rather unusual alliance, Cabot Corporation, a major manufacturer of carbon black, agreed to "50% ownership in Malaysia and Iran, and in Brazil it sought an equity share lower than one-half so as to be legally able to charge technical fees to its Brazilian affiliate" Goulet, 1989, p.55). Still, other MNCs remain less tolerant of joint ventures that require substantial, not to mention controlling interest held by host Third World partners. These corporations may prefer to have firms in the Third World manufacture or market their products under a licensing agreement.

Licensing Agreements

"Under a licensing agreement, a firm allows another company to use its brand name, trademark, technology, patent, copyrights, or other expertise" (Griffin, 1990, p.794). The licensee in this case agrees to operate under specified conditions in addition to the payment of fees and royalties. The fees and royalties are usually based on a percentage of sales or value-added.

Licensing relationships can be between independent business enterprises, parent companies and wholly or partially owned subsidiaries, and joint ventures between private and/or public firms. The dominant form of licensing occurs between MNCs and their affiliates in Third World countries. This is also the most suitable arrangement for transfer pricing. With improving absorptive capacity, increasing number of Third World firms are signing licensing contracts with foreign MNCs as a technique to expand innovation domestically. Larson and Anderson (1994) observed that "Licensing arrangements are generally associated with a greater degree of local, post transfer innovation relative to other forms of transfer" (p.548). Executives of MNCs reveal that licensing is hardly a major income earner; its attraction, they point out, is that it enables them to:

- Obtain supplementary earnings from technologies whose period of competitive advantage in primary home markets is drawing to a close;
- Gain access to markets where direct investment is excluded, either by formal policy, general practice, or specific discrimination;
- Seize opportunities to improve a technology in special circumstances which approximate those found in Third World markets;
- Gain the goodwill of selected governments by supplying them with technology even if the economic advantages of doing so are not great (seeking to maintain 'friendly' relations which can be useful in other domains;
- Obtain side benefits in the form of favorable corporate publicity. (Goulet, 1989, p.56)

As noted earlier, as Third World countries gain in domestic technological capability, they are turning increasingly to licensing arrangements as a method of furthering domestic innovation. Japan, for example, made extensive use of licensing in its socioeconomic transformation into a world economic power. Where a country is interested in running a production facility after it is set up by a foreign source, the appropriate mode of transfer of choice may be a turnkey project.

Turnkey Projects

The last technology transfer technique is known as a turnkey project. A turnkey project is one in which a foreign organization undertakes the construction of a production facility and turns the key to a domestic firm or some other organization when the facility is ready for operation. "Investments funded by international organizations and government agencies are basically of the turnkey nature" (Stewart, Jr. and Nihei, 1987, p.11). Turnkey projects usually are more suited to a single activity production facility such as a cement factory, a sugar refinery, a steel mill, etc. Several Indian steel mills were initiated through turnkey operations (Elkan, 1973). A turnkey project may also include the training of domestic personnel to take over the operation of the factory eventually. It is worth noting that in a turnkey investment domestic personnel are able to operate the new plant but may lack the ability to set up a cement factory or a sugar refinery. The ability to reproduce or set up a production plant may indeed be more beneficial in terms of fostering self-sustaining development in the long run than having one from a turnkey arrangement in which the recipient only consumes or operates the technology involved.

Concluding Remarks

The focus of this chapter has been on explaining the concept of technology and the conditions in which it can be more beneficial to Third World countries. It is important to understand that technology is not valued for its own sake, but in the expectation that it will bring about the well being of the masses. Technology, in its role as a means of change, must not be confused with the end being pursued, which is the socioeconomic development of people. Technology is only a passive resource whose effectiveness depends on an active human resource capital. To take advantage of technology as a potent source of positive change, Third World countries must work hard on their absorptive capacity. It is erroneous to speak of technology transfer if the ability of Third World countries to assimilate, adapt, modify, and create technology is limited or nonexistent. Channels of technology transfer such as the MNCs will train Third World workers only to the extent it enables them to maximize profits. By their nature MNCs do not operate to make Third World countries self-sufficient, self-reliant, and able to do "their own thing." Training domestic labor to be able to operate production facilities does not put them in a position to produce capital goods and does not automatically prepare them to be able to set up production facilities on their own. It is the ability to create and accumulate national capital, to set up the necessary infrastructure and the ability to operate and maintain them that promotes self-sustained development. The importance of producing domestic vocational education graduates, technicians, technologists, engineers, scientists, and entrepreneurs, as sources of a country's absorptive capacity cannot be stressed enough. Any country that hopes to develop a modern industrial system will realize sooner or later that developing this cadre of professionals is an indispensable requirement. Without these professionals in place to establish the foundational technical developments upon which the prosperity of a country depends, attempts to develop socially, economically, politically, and technologically will be no more than a false start. As experience has shown, this approach to development only serves to perpetuate Third World dependence on the West. It is perhaps appropriate to end with a quote that captures the message of this chapter: "A

country's comparative advantage increasingly lies in its ability to use effectively new technology, which is generally a function of the capacity of its population to absorb
new technologies and incorporate them in the production process" (Aharoni, 1991, p.80).

References

Aggarwal, R. (1991). Technology transfer and economic growth: A historical perspective on current developments. In T. Agmon and M. A. Von Glinow (Eds.), Technology transfer in international business (pp. 56-78), New York, NY: Oxford University Press, Inc.

Aharoni, Y. (1991). Education and technology transfer: Recipient point of view. In T. Agmon and M. A. Von Glinow (Eds.), Technology transfer in international business (pp. 79-102), New York, NY: Oxford University Press, Inc.

Akubue, A. I. (2002). Technology transfer: A Third World perspective. The Journal of Technology Studies, XXVII (1), 14-21.

Akubue, A. I. & Pytlik, E. (1991, Winter/Spring). Technology, technical, and vocational education in Nigeria: Past neglect and present attention. Journal of Epsilon Pi Tau, 43-48.

Certo, S. C. (1986). Principles of modern management (3rd ed.). Dubuque, Iowa: Wm. C. Brown Publishers.

Diwan, R. K. & Livingston, D. (1979). Alternative development strategies and appropriate technology: Science policy for an equitable world. Elmsford, NY: Pergamon Press, Inc.

Elkan, W. (1973). An introduction to development economics. Middlesex, England: Penquin Books Ltd.

Emmanuel, A. (1982). Appropriate or underdeveloped technology? New York: John Wiley & Sons.

Goulet, D. (1989). <u>The uncertain promise: Value conflicts in technology transfer</u> (New ed.). New York, NY: New Horizons Press.

Grieve, R. H. (2004). Appropriate technology in a globalizing world. International Journal of Technology Management and Sustainable Development, 3 (3), 173187.

Griffin, R. W. (1990). <u>Management</u>. (3rd ed.). Boston, MA: Houghton Mifflin Company.

Jequier, N. (1976). <u>Appropriate technology: Problems and promises</u>. Paris, France: O.E.C.D.

Kaynak, E. (1985). Transferof technology from developed to developing countries: Some insights from Turkey. In A. C. Samli (Ed.), <u>Technology transfer</u> (pp. 155-176). New York, NY: Quorum Books.

Lall, S. (1992). Technological capabilities and industrialization. <u>World Development</u>, <u>20</u>(2), 165-186.

Larson, B. A. & Anderson, M. (1994, August). Technology transfer, licensing contracts, and incentives for further innovation. <u>American Journal of Agricultural Economics</u>, <u>76</u>, 547-556.

Mallampally, P. & Sauvant, K. P. (1999). Foreign direct investment in developing countries, <u>Finance & Development</u>, <u>36</u>(1), 34-37.

Mason, M. (1997). Development and disorder: A history of the Third World since 1945. Hanover, NH: University Press of New England.

Meier, G. M. (1984). Emerging from poverty: The economics that really matters. New York, NY: Oxford University Press, Inc.

Mittelman, J. H. & Pasha, M. K. (1997). Out from underdevelopment revisited. Changing global structures and the remaking of the Third World. New York, NY: St. Martin" Press.

Nurkse, R. (1961). Equilibrium and growth in the world economy. Cambridge, MA: Harvard University Press.

Pacey, A. (1990). Technology in world civilization: A thousand-year history. Cambridge, MA: The MIT Press.

Pellegrini, U. (1979). The problem of appropriate technology. In A. DeGiorgio & C. Roveda (Eds.), Criteria for selecting appropriate technologies under different cultural, technical and social conditions (pp. 1-5). New York, NY: Pergamon Press.

Pytlik, E. C., Lauda, D. P., & Johnson, D. L. (1985). Technology, change and society. Worcester, MA: Davis Publications, Inc.

Rosenberg, N. (1972). Technology and American economic growth. New York, NY: Harper & Row.

Schumacher, E. F. (1973). Small is beautiful: Economics as if people mattered. New York, NY: Harper & Row.

Sharif, N. (1992). Technological dimensions of international cooperation and sustainable development. <u>Technological Forecasting and Social Change</u>, <u>42</u>(4), 367-383.

Siddiqi, M. (2001, January). Luring the investor. (foreign direct investment), <u>African Business</u>, 14-16.

Simon, D. (1991). International business and the transborder movement of technology: A dialectical perspective. In T. Agmon & M. A. V. Glinow (Eds.), <u>Technology transfer in international business</u> (pp. 5-28), New York, NY: Oxford University Press, Inc.

Stewart, Jr. C. T. & Nihei, Y. (1987). <u>Technology transfer and human factors</u>. Lexington, MA: D. C. Heath & Company.

Stolp, C. (1993, March). Technology, development, and hemispheric free trade. <u>The Annals of the American Academy</u>, <u>526</u>, 151-163.

United Nations (1983). <u>Transnational corporations in world development</u>. (ST/CTC/46). New York, NY: Author.

Volti, R. (2001). Society and technological change (4th ed.). New York, NY: Worth Publishers.

Wiens, A. E. and Wiens, K. S. (1996). Technology and the quality of life: Introductory perspectives. In R. L. Custer & A. E. Wiens (Eds.), Technology and the quality of life (pp. 1-42). Peoria, IL: Glencoe/McGraw-Hill.

Willoughby, K. W. (1990). Technology choice: A critique of the appropriate technology movement. Boulder, CO: Westview Press.

Chapter SIX

Appropriate Technology: Widening the Technological Options for Third World Development

Introduction

Persistent social and economic problems in Third World countries, despite decades of massive infusion of advanced technology from the industrial world, continue to raise questions concerning the appropriateness of this technology. Problems of poverty, unemployment, inequality, and basic needs fulfillment are common facts of life today in many Third World countries. These conditions have increased the urgency of engaging a development trajectory that de-emphasizes growth and technological monoculture. The technological option for this development paradigm has been variously called intermediate, progressive, alternative, light-capital, labor-intensive, indigenous, appropriate, low-cost, community, soft, radical, liberatory, and convivial technology. However, appropriate technology, for reasons that will be addressed later, has emerged as the all-embracing rubric representing the viewpoints associated with all the other terms.

The purpose of this chapter is to discuss appropriate technology as it concerns technological, social and economic development in the Third World. Critics and proponents of appropriate technology have made claims and counter-claims about its strengths and weaknesses. Not surprisingly, some of these claims are often based on prejudice, ignorance, or intolerance

(Kaplinsky, 1990; Willoughby, 1990; Jequier, 1976). The view espoused here is that the international and intra-national disparities in the level of development of the Third World are so great that any suggestion of inflexibility in the technological and socioeconomic development strategy employed would be grossly unrealistic. Third World development must not take an either/or stance regarding technology input; it requires widening the technological options available to countries.

Some Compelling Issues

The conventional development strategy for the Third World is and has been dominated by economic growth. Consequently, industrialization induced by capital accumulation and technology transfer from Europe, North America, and Japan to the Third World were pursued with little or no consideration to enlist other more relevant strategies. Decades of massive importation of advanced technology and the implementation of large-scale, capital-intensive production methods in Third World countries have revealed some shortcomings of such an approach. First of all, the strategy entails the employment of capital-intensive technology in countries that are short of capital and endowed with surplus labor. Third World countries, by opting for capital-intensive production technology in spite of their shortage of capital, can only afford to create a few jobs for a small number of people due to a very high capital/labor ratio. This implies that several Third World countries equip only a very small proportion of their labor force with the means of increasing production. In this case, small islands of high productivity emerge in core urban centers at the expense or neglect of the periphery involving the more populous traditional sector of the economy. The result has been the creation of a dual economic structure (consisting of a prosperous modern sector and an impoverished traditional sector), worsening unemployment conditions, and widespread abject poverty in many Third World countries. According to a 1976 United States Agency for International Development (USAID) proposal to the United States Congress, the effects of capital-intensive technology are not limited to problems of unemployment in the Third World. "The high capital cost of modern technology has also contributed to the development of dual economies small, relatively well-off enclaves of high productivity and well-paid workers side by side with relative stagnation among the larger community" (Thormann, 1979, p. 282). There are writers who attribute growing poverty in the Third World in part to rapid growth in the modern sector that is sustained with the most advanced imported technology (Singer, 1985). This growth in Third World metropolitan areas is often accompanied with little or no spread effect to the sectors in the periphery. Commenting on this issue, Robinson (1979) observed that "a growth strategy that takes the form of industry-led development, using the technologies that are appropriate for Western societies, leaves almost untouched in the rural areas increasing absolute numbers of impoverished and underemployed workers" (p. xii). It is because this growth has failed to create sufficient employment opportunities and the growing disparity in progress between regions that concerns have been raised about the conventional development strategy. The World Bank even touched on the inevitability of getting priorities right in terms of the pattern of development that best addresses the needs of the Third World:

> *The choice to be faced ... is whether to invest heavily in a few workers and in services for a few to increase their production and living standards substantially, leaving the rest unaffected by growth (or at best affected indirectly), or whether to make some gain in the productivity of many people by investments at lower per capita affecting the mass of the people in the country. (Willoughby, 1990, p. 118)*

As mentioned earlier, an impact of the pattern of growth in metropolitan areas of the Third World is the development of a dual economy. This has been blamed for causing, among other things, a constant influx of people into the cities from the rural sector. Not only is this rural-urban migration a threat to the economy of the rural sector, but is also to the survival of the modern sector as it struggles to cope with exploding urban population.

The modern sector is the creation of mostly advanced, capital-intensive technology imported from the rich industrialized countries. Schumacher (1973) blamed this technology for creating what he called the "process of mutual poisoning" in most of the Third World. This is a condition in which the concentration of industrial development in Third World cities adversely affects the economy of the traditional sector as people abandon their traditional socioeconomic undertakings to move to the cities. This movement in turn affects the cities adversely by overpopulating them and causing problems almost impossible to manage. The relationship in this case becomes one of mutual destruction. This manifests itself today in the Third World in the form of high rates of unemployment, poverty, great income disparity, and declining access to basic needs. This being the case, a major challenge today in the Third World is to articulate an effective approach to improve conditions in Third World countries, making sure that benefits from development are within people's reach regardless of where they live. It is called appropriate to suggest among other things that it should meet the basic needs of poor people in developing societies (Day and Croxton, 1993). Appropriate technology is intended to address social and economic problems, especially in the rural and informal sectors of the Third World. Stewart (1985) perhaps put the need for appropriate technology in perspective in the following statement:

> *The argument for appropriate technology is not that jobs should be put before output, but that techniques can be developed which promote both. Appropriate technology is intended to raise productivity and incomes outside the advanced technology sector and so extend the benefits of development throughout the population. (p. 28)*

It goes without saying that using appropriate technology to stimulate production and employment in the sectors outside the core urban areas so important an objective that it ought to be seen as a national imperative. It is unreasonable not to promote appropriate technology for development in the traditional and informal sectors in view of the capital and foreign exchange situation in many Third

World societies. Development in these regions must start with less complex and expensive techniques and move forward.

Development Path

Communities, societies, or countries have evolved historically with the type of technology that reflects their level of development and factor endowment. For example, the capital stock of the United States late in the 18th century consisted of hand pumps, Franklin stoves, wooden plows and draft animals (Norwine and Gonzalez, 1988). During the reign of Mao Tse-tung communist China turned to appropriate technology for rural development after a major disagreement led to a break up with Russia in 1960. China's policies on development changed during the period of Cultural Revolution to include the phrase 'walking on two legs.' This entailed the encouragement of technological dualism for the simultaneous development of large-scale and small-scale undertakings to promote industrialization nationwide in China (Pacey, 1990; Riskin, 1979). While concentration in the urban areas was on building large-scale, capital-intensive factories, the focus in the rural areas was on the development of small-scale industries based on appropriate technology. In this new approach "rural small-scale industrialization depended in a fundamental way on the prior and continuing successful development of urban large-scale industry" (Perkins, 1980, p. 187). The rural industries, making use of intermediate technology, were expected to take advantage of the country's abundant local resources, including industrial waste or scrap from the large-scale, city-based factories (Riskin, 1979). The uniqueness of this new direction, however, is that it emphasized the decentralization of production, the reliance on domestic initiatives, and the pursuit of self-sufficiency. Writers like Dwight H. Perkins have argued that China's encouragement of small-scale industries making use of appropriate technology in the rural areas created jobs and enabled the country "to avoid some of the worst aspects of the urban-rural polarization that characterizes so many developing countries" (Long, 1980, p. 7).

However, before China's 'walking on two legs' and 'relying on its own forces' (Jequier, 1976; Dunn, 1978) initiative, the concept of appropriate technology had long been an important part of India's village industries even before the 1930s. One of India's early pioneers and practitioners of appropriate technology was its moral leader and advocate of nonviolent resistance Mohandas Karamchand Gandhi. Gandhi's familiarity with the work of Henry David Thoreau of the United Sates exerted great influence in shaping his philosophy of development. In fact, a number of writers on appropriate technology have variously referred to Gandhi as the 'father' of appropriate technology and the 'first appropriate technologist' (Betz et al, 1984; Rybczynski, 1980), knowing full well that the phrase gained common usage only after Gandhi's time. As Rybczynski (1980) pointed out, "it was Gandhi who, before China's Mao Tse-tung, recognized that the peasants should be the basis for economic development in Asia" (p. 37). Gandhi spoke incessantly of the need for village industries in India, while maintaining that India's survival and future were dependent on the state of the villages where most Indians reside. Underlying Gandhi's notion of village industries was his epigrammatic expression that "the poor of the world cannot be helped by mass production, [but] only production by the masses" (Schumacher, 1973, p. 153). From Gandhi's perspective, any concern with goods requires mass production, but concern with people necessitates production by the masses. The Charkha (spinning wheel) was Gandhi's ideal appropriate technology device, and he saw in it a symbol of freedom, self-reliance, and a technical means that was right for India. The idea of technology discriminately enriching a minority of people at the expense of the majority or putting masses of people out of work to increase profit was in Gandhi's view counterproductive and unacceptable. However, Gandhi was not uncompromising in his rejection of large-scale, capital-intensive industrial enterprises. Modern-sector industrial development, in Gandhi's view, should supplement and reinforce the development of small-scale industries and agriculture in the hinterland. In a quote credited to Gandhi, he expressed his choice of the development path suited to the Indian sub-continent:

If I can covert the country to my point of view, the social order of the future will be based predominantly on the Charkha and all it implies. It will include everything that promotes the well-being of the villagers. I do visualize electricity, ship-building, ironworks, machine-making and the like existing side by side with village handicrafts. But the order of dependence will be reversed. Hitherto, the industrialization has been so planned as to destroy the villages and the village crafts. In the State of the future it will subserve the villages and their crafts.... (Bhatt, 1980, p. 172)

Gandhi moved to start India in this development path by founding organizations such as the 'All India Spinners Association' and 'All India Village Industries Association' (Dunn, 1978). A group known as Gandhian economists later founded the Appropriate Technology Association of India, one of the early appropriate technology organizations. Prominent among the non-Indians who shared Gandhi's philosophy was Dr. Ernst Friedrich "Fritz" Schumacher, who later played a key role in popularizing appropriate technology worldwide.

From Gandhi to Schumacher

Before becoming a respected leader in the appropriate technology movement, Schumacher was a well-established economist. In fact, Schumacher's work as a top professional economist is believed to have influenced such great economist as John Maynard Keynes. According to Willoughby (1990), Keynes' wish before his death was for his mantle to fall on either of two people Otto Clarke or Fritz Schumacher: "Otto Clarke," he said, "can do anything with figures, but Schumacher can make them sing" (p. 57). Both Clarke and Schumacher worked with Keynes for the British Treasury. Later experience convinced Schumacher to become an ardent advocate of a different technological and socioeconomic development path.

Born in Bonn, West Germany, in 1911, Schumacher moved to England in the late 1930s. As a German immigrant in Britain, he endured a period of trial and tribulation during World War II. In the end, Schumacher distinguished himself as a great economist and worked in different capacities for various British establishments, including the position he held for more than twenty years as Senior Economist and Economic Advisor to the British National Coal Board (NCB) from 1950 (Schumacher, 1974; Willoughby, 1990; Kaplinsky, 1990). His experience as an employee of the NCB persuaded Schumacher to reconsider his support of large-scale organizations.

> *Schumacher was first sensitized to the problems of scale by the NCB's attitude to the problems of pneumoconiosis [black lung disease], a lethal disease of the lungs associated with coal mining. Instead of recognizing the self-evident health consequences of coal mining, the NCB chose to defend itself rigorously and to fight (and subsequently win) the legal argument on technicalities. In saving itself relatively small sums of compensation (2 – 3 million Pound Sterling), Schumacher believed that the NCB had ceased to concern itself with people. More importantly, he believed that such uncaring attitudes were not exceptional but were an inevitable consequence of the organization's scale. (Kaplinsky, 1990, p. 137)*

Schumacher's new philosophy was further shaped from a 1955 trip to Burma (today's Myanmar), where he served under the United Nations as Economic Adviser to U Nu, the country's Prime Minister at the time (Crittenden, 1975; Rybczynski, 1980; Schumacher, 1974; Willoughby, 1990). While in Burma he experienced an economic setting quite unlike what he was used to in Germany, Britain, and the United States. With a very low GDP per capita in Burma, which would be an indication of poverty from a Western view, Schumacher was amazed that the Burmese went about their daily lives apparently quite happy and content. Living in Burma also revealed to him some of the inadequacies of a growth-based conventional development strategy. Such a strategy encouraging the use of capital-intensive technology from the industrialized societies was having some harmful consequences in Burma and other Third World countries. These observations, among others, led Schumacher to the conclusion that the "problems of economics do not have any final solution, because they are human problems, that can be 'solved' only within a particular set of circumstances for a particular time and particular place" (Cornish, 1974, pp. 276 – 277). Living in Burma also brought Schumacher in contact with Buddhist economics, one of the most influential forces behind his thinking and ideas. Another major occurrence while Schumacher was in Burma was his discovery of Gandhi, a man he later called the 'greatest economist of the twentieth century' (Crittenden, 1975). According to Crittenden (1975), Schumacher was a self-proclaimed 'indiscriminate thief of ideas,' who credited much of his ideas about development and preservation of the natural environment to Jesus, the Buddha, and Gandhi. In subsequent years, through contacts and familiarity with Gandhi's work, Schumacher developed the ideas and reputation that earned him an invitation to Hyderabad, India in the early 1960s. While in India at the invitation of the Indian Planning Commission and his friend Jayaprakash J. Narayan, he gave a seminar on *Technologies for Small Industries in Rural Areas* (Dunn, 1978). His visit to India was a welcomed opportunity for Schumacher, for he was able to study Gandhi's approach at close range and met with acclaimed Gandhian economists.

The Birth of Intermediate Technology

Frustrated with large-scale organizations and buoyed by his experience in Burma and India, Schumacher developed the ideas behind the concept of intermediate technology, which became the linchpin of his seminal book *Small is Beautiful: Economics as if People Mattered*, published in 1973. Perhaps, more than the others, Gandhi's work exerted the most influence on Schumacher. In using the term intermediate technology, Schumacher envisioned a technology for the Third World that was midway between, for example, a hand hoe and a tractor. As Schumacher (1973) described it, "Such an intermediate technology would be immensely more productive than the indigenous technology, but it would be immensely cheaper than the sophisticated, highly capital-intensive technology of modern industry" (p. 180). The concept of intermediate technology, to be considered compatible, must meet the challenges outlined in the following propositions:

- Workplaces have to be created in the areas where the people are living now, and not primarily in metropolitan areas into which they tend to migrate;

- These workplaces must be, on average, cheap enough so that they can be created in large numbers without this calling for an unattainable level of capital formation and imports;

- The production methods employed must be relatively simple, so that the demands for high skills are minimized, not only in the production process itself but also in matters of organization, raw material supply, financing, marketing, and so forth;

- Production should be mainly from local materials and mainly for local use. (Schumacher, 1973, pp. 175-176)

To tackle these challenges, Schumacher and his colleagues founded the Intermediate Technology Development Group (ITDG) now known by its new name of Practical Action in London in 1965 (Schumacher, 1974). Since its inception, the ITDG has been serving to provide information on existing low-cost, labor-intensive technologies, create nonexistent technological innovations, and publish important how-to-do manuals on affordable do-it-yourself work methods. The organization has also been responsible for convening major conferences on simple, low-cost technologies for small-scale industries. For example, there was a 1968 trail-blazing conference convened at Oxford University. The aim of this conference was to promote intermediate technology for Third World development and enlist industrial involvement in its development (Rybczynski, 1980). As it happened, one of the issues raised at the conference was the necessity of a name change. Intermediate technology was viewed to be suggestive of a technology that was inferior or second-rate (Kaplinsky, 1990; Willoughby, 1990), and conveyed only the economic and engineering aspects of innovation. The term was further "criticized for implying a technological fix for development problems, separate from the social and political factors involved" (Hollick, 1982, p. 214). This orientation incorrectly regarded technology only as artifact, making appropriate technology in development essentially technocratic. As a result, engineers and economists were left in charge to decide for a passive audience of poor communities which machines were right for what scale of operation and which were simple to operate and maintain (Day and Croxton, 1993). It must be noted that the ITDG group has carried out needed policy changes and has dropped this practice in favor of enlisting the active involvement of local communities in the process of technology design and development, otherwise known as participatory technology development. Also dropped in favor of more autonomous management responsibility for local project work was the practice of project management by UK-based staff and country offices. These necessary policy changes are in accord with the organization's recent name change to Practical Action, while leaving intact established organizational values such as finding and applying practical answers to poverty, sustainable solutions, and the focus on people rather than statistical numbers and growth at all costs. The phrase "Technology Challenging Poverty" is often used in association with the new name (http://practicalaction.org/print.php?id=practicalaction, 2007).

The phrase appropriate technology was suggested at the 1968 conference as a substitute, in part because it reflects the social and cultural dimensions of innovation (Pellegrini, 1979), and, unlike intermediate technology, for not carrying the connotation of inferiority. The rationale was that with appropriate technology the chances of its acceptance by those for whom it was intended would be greatly improved. Although intermediate technology is still used, appropriate technology has become the popular and more widely used appellation. The world owes the appropriate technology movement to Gandhi and Schumacher, who are widely acknowledged as its progenitors. Schumacher's role in turning appropriate technology into a household phrase cannot go unacknowledged. So outstanding was this contribution by a single individual that Rybczynski (1980) even opined that "E. F. Schumacher was undoubtedly the motive force behind the appropriate technology movement. It is not an exaggeration to say that without him there would have been no appropriate technology" (p. 6). Individual feelings apart, E. F. Schumacher, through his passion and dedication to the cause, established himself as a leading authority on appropriate technology.

What is Appropriate Technology?

Appropriate technology may have been practiced for many generations in the past, but there is something new about it today; it has evolved into a development approach aimed at tackling community development problems. Viewed in this way, appropriate technology cannot be seen simply as some identifiable technical devices; rather, it is an approach to community development consisting of a body of knowledge, techniques, and an underlying philosophy. In fact, Dunn (1978) called it a complete systems approach to development that is both self-adaptive and dynamic, which is saying that as its users become wealthier and more skilled they can both afford and also use more expensive technical means. As Hazeltine and Bull (1999) noted, the experience of countries like the United States "appears to confirm that one of the advantages of appropriate technology is that it can be an effective way to shift to modern technology" (p. 277). In this case, appropriate technology can only be considered evolutionary and not static. It follows, then, that as appropriate technology improves the productive capabilities of a community, the community influences and improves the level of technology as well. In this book, appropriate technology is defined as an approach to development that not only emphasizes job creation and optimum use of existing skills and resources but it also builds on those skills and resources to raise the productive capacity of a community without destroying native cultures and the environment. This definition, among others, delineates the environmental, economic, and social expectations and/or objectives of appropriate technology. The environmental objective is concerned with the long-term sustainability of development; the economic objective concerns the satisfaction of basic human needs and the reduction of inequalities; and the social objective is concerned with the promotion of endogenous self-reliance through social participation (Reddy, 1979).

Other definitions by different writers have contributed significantly to a better understanding of appropriate technology.

Other Definitions of Appropriate Technology

The proposal mentioned earlier for the development and dissemination of appropriate technology in the Third World was prepared and submitted to special U.S. Congressional Committees by the USAID in June1976. This proposal featured the following description of appropriate technology.

> *In terms of available resources, appropriate technologies are intensive in the use of the abundant factor, labor, economical in the use of scarce factors, capital and highly trained personnel, and intensive in the use of domestically produced inputs. In terms of small production units, appropriate technologies are small-scale but efficient, replicable in numerous units, readily operated, maintained and repaired, low-cost and accessible to low-income persons. In terms of the people who use or benefit from them, appropriate technologies seek to be compatible with local cultural and social environments. (Thormann, 1979, 283 – 284)*

Another interesting and enlightening description of appropriate technology is one by Bourrieres (1979), who presented it as:

one which uses the largest number of people as they are, with the training they have had and with their actual technical and financial aspirations. But while technology must correspond as closely as possible to actual manpower supply, teaching and training methods should endeavor to improve that supply so as to meet the requirements of the most productive technologies. (p. 5)

Pellegrini (1979) suggested that a technology should be considered appropriate "when its introduction into a community creates a self-reinforcing process internal to the same community, which supports the growth of the local activities and the development of indigenous capabilities as decided by the community itself" p. 2).

Paul Harrison, a freelance journalist specializing in Third World development issues, stated that:

Appropriate technology means simply any technology that makes the most economical use of a country's natural resources and its relative proportions of capital, labor and skills, and that furthers national and social goals. Fostering AT means consciously encouraging the right choice of technology, not simply letting businessmen make the decision for you. (Harrison, 1980, p. 140)

Economist Michael P. Todaro defined appropriate technology as:

Technology that is appropriate for existing factor endowments. For example, a technology employing a higher proportion of labor relative to other factors in a labor-abundant economy is usually more appropriate than one that uses smaller labor proportions relative to other factors. (Todaro, 1997, p. 667)

Writing in the Economic Journal, Morawetz (1974) defined appropriate technology as the "set of techniques which makes optimum use of available resources in a given environment..." (p. 517).

In the definition by Betz et al (1984), appropriate technology was defined as:

> *Providing technical solutions that are appropriate to the economic structure of those influenced: to their ability to finance the activity, to their ability to operate and maintain the facility, to the environmental conditions involved, and to the management capabilities of the population. (p. 3)*

Other definitions list specific characteristics of appropriate technology. Take the definition by Jequier and Blanc (1983) for example:

> *Appropriate technology (AT) is now recognized as the generic term for a wide range of technologies characterized by any one or several of the following characteristics: low investment cost per workplace, low capital investment per unit of output, organizational simplicity, high adaptability to a peculiar social and cultural environment, sparing use of natural resources, low cost of final product or high potential for employment. (p. 10)*

Characteristics of Appropriate Technology

The last definition does not just suggest the criteria for technological appropriateness; it also implies that there is such a thing as inappropriate technology. Such characteristics have been well documented by various writers and appropriate technologists (Schumacher, 1973; Darrow and Saxenian, 1986; Dunn, 1978; Evans and Alder, 1979; Hazeltine & Bull, 1999; Carley and Christie, 1993; Jequier, 1983; Congdon, 1977), and as a result will not be treated in depth here. The appropriateness of technology is not limited only to job creation, using local resources, and utilizing renewable energy resources; it is also about being affordable, easy to maintain, compatible with existing infrastructure, efficient in the use of scarce

Bio-gas digesters are used for energy production. Picture on right shows the barn housing cattle in the background. Picture on left shows the methane stove powered by the digester.

natural resources, environmentally benign, and partial to small-scale. To many, appropriate technology is always small, simple, cheap, and labor-intensive. Perhaps E. F. Schumacher, more than anybody else, contributed to that general perception. However, Anderson (1985) made the point that "scale, complexity and expense are not always positively correlated; it is possible for a large machine to be both simple and cheap and for a small one to be highly complex and expensive" (p. 68). It is not generally acknowledged that Schumacher expressed a similar idea about the issue of scale. For example, he stated: "Whether a given industrial activity is appropriate to the conditions of a developing district does not directly depend on 'scale,' but on the technology employed" (Schumacher, 1973, p. 179). It is conceivable that Schumacher's commitment to smallness of scale was provisional rather than absolute, and may have had more to do perhaps with the prevailing idolatry of bigness still evident in today's technological society than anything else. Toffler (1980) disclosed that "Schumacher once told friends that, had he lived in a world of small organizations, he would have written a book called *Big Is Beautiful*" (p. 247).

Widening Technological Options

The characteristics or criteria of appropriate technology discussed above are not meant to imply that there is a perfect technology or a panacea that can resolve all the socioeconomic problems of the Third World at once. The fact remains that circumstances vary from one Third World society to another, and what is appropriate for one country or social setting may not necessarily be appropriate for the other. As Willoughby (1990) pointed out, "the concept of appropriate technology attempts to discriminate between different technologies according to their relative suitability for specific purposes or situations" (p. 6). Appropriate technology is not about taking a stand against technology, but about technology encompassing a collection of social and technical options rather than just a physical phenomenon. From this collection, the best choices are then made based on the objectives to be accomplished and possible human and environmental effects. The notion of appropriate technology suggests that all options

Hand tools are the norm in many third world rural settings. The animal powered plow is a significant technological advance for many farmers yet hand fashioned tools are still prevelant.

should be researched for 'best fit.' "The view that developing countries should, as a general strategy, seek labor-intensive techniques and turn their backs on advanced-country technology is, at best, naïve, and, at worst, counter-productive, particularly in view of current trends in the world economy" (Grieve, 2004, p. 176). This view is also an exaggerated and misleading interpretation of the intent of appropriate technology. It is not realistic to suggest that the development of the Third World should be based almost entirely on technological monoculture. One must keep in mind that the primary focus of appropriate technology is in rural and informal sectors of the Third World. This is in recognition that economic growth in the past several years has tended to be confined to the urban modern sector in part because of capital and foreign exchange shortage. Interestingly, campaigns against appropriate technology are usually spearheaded not by the poor who stand to benefit the most from its use, but by the rich and powerful elite group. The elite of the Third World are not the "poverty-stricken multitudes who lack any real basis of existence, whether in rural or in urban areas, who have neither the 'best' nor the 'second best' but go short of even the most essential means of subsistence" (Schumacher, 1973, p. 181). This is why the case has to be made for widening the pool of available technology for use in the Third World.

Since differences in the level of development and factor endowments do exist between and within countries, the notion that 'one size fits all' definitely does not apply. Today's intolerance of pluralism in global technological development is comparable to a situation once in the former Soviet Union about footwear production. As Ernst F. Schumacher wrote in Crittenden (1975), "we have been like the Soviets who made 500 million pairs of shoes, all the same size, and said, 'take it or leave it—this is the only way we know how to do it'" (p. F5). Widening the pool of available technology for Third World development can satisfy the needs of both the rich and poor of the Third World and promote participation for the poor in the development process. Brooks (1980) suggested along the same lines that "appropriate

Photo-voltaic cells bring power to remote areas of developing countries.

technology and current technology are complementary rather than mutually exclusive, and that the potential benefits of both will be enhanced when they coexist" (p. 54). From the foregoing discussion, it is clear that there is certainly an urgent need to expand the scope of technology and to integrate appropriate technology in the development of the Third World. However, appropriate technology has its critics.

Criticisms of Appropriate Technology

Appropriate technology has been the subject of numerous criticisms despite its obvious advantages. Common among the criticisms is the claim that appropriate technology is inefficient, a technology not congenial to growth and improving standard of living. Often failed projects based on appropriate technology are cited as evidence in support of this criticism, as if any technology enjoys immunity from failure. Rybczynski (1980) cited cases of biogas digesters in India and South Korea that were abandoned either because they produced insufficient methane or for inadequate supply of cow dung as evidence of inefficient appropriate technology. This account only tells part of the story. A government *National Project on Biogas Development* in 1981 brought needed relief to many in rural India. For instance, biogas in Pura, a village in south India, has been meeting the water-pumping, electric-lighting, cooking, and fertilizer needs of this village's 485 inhabitants (Sampat, 1995). According to Sampat (1995), about 2 million biogas digesters have been installed in India since 1981, "and although the program has had its share of problems, it has made substantial progress" (p. 21). Appropriate technology may not be efficient from an engineering standpoint, but it is pedantic and unrealistic to describe any technology that enhances the capacity to satisfy community goals and aspirations as inefficient. A related criticism claims that workplace productivity is compromised with appropriate technology. This argument implicitly suggests that output per worker is unimportant to appropriate technology. The fact is that appropriate technologists understand the important correlation between productivity and standard of living.

On the other hand, it must be realized that given the endemic unemployment situation in most Third World societies the maximization of job opportunities is not a matter of subordinate priority either. It is possible that the effort to maximize productivity in the urban areas can be pursued simultaneously with the effort to maximize work opportunities for the unemployed and underemployed in the traditional and informal sectors. The issue is not about opting for either productivity or job creation, but, as mentioned earlier, finding a good mix of techniques to promote both and to ensure a far-reaching distribution of the benefits of development. Furthermore, critics have made arguments of the kind that if appropriate technology is as effective as some of its advocates claim, it should have no difficulty displacing the dominant, capital-intensive technology. These critics advance the notion that the prevailing technology at any one time is the most efficient possible for that time (Kaplinsky, 1990; Brooks, 1980; Rosenbrock, 1979). This is probably one of those arguments based on the assumption of a 'free market' and a qualifying ceteris paribus. It sounds quite presumptuous and too sanguine to completely rule out the possibility that the dominant technology may by chance not be the most efficient or effective. However, it is possible to sustain a wasteful technology through government intervention, institutional inertia, the actions of vested interest groups, years of enormous investment, and established position of the technology, all of which may be prejudicial to the development of alternatives. Given this possibility, Rosenbrock (1979) surmised that "It is quite conceivable that a worse solution could be perpetuated indefinitely this way…" (p. 9). One final criticism of appropriate technology is the claim that it is an inferior technology and a part of a scheme by Western industrialized countries to maintain their position of socioeconomic and technological dominance over the Third World (Thormann, 1980; Willoughby, 1990; Kaplinsky, 1990). Whether this allegation is believable or not depends on one's perspective. Perhaps it is worth mentioning here that:

> *There is no evidence that a country which starts with simple technology cannot move into more complex technology, and there*

is much evidence that for countries starting with a simple technology the transition to industrialization was easier than it was for those that shifted directly to a complicated case. (Hazeltine and Bull, 1999, p. 277)

One must bear in mind that appropriate technology as defined by its proponents is a technology tailored to serve the particular needs of a given region or community. This implies that a painstaking effort is made to secure the 'best' alternative there is for the set of circumstances peculiar to that region or community. So, "if one wished to have the best technology for given circumstances it would be absurd to advocate inferior technology and doubly absurd to call it 'appropriate', when, logically, it would not be the best available" (Willoughby, 1990, p. 237). Willoughby (1990) put it more succinctly:

Many criticisms of Appropriate Technology are based upon either ignorance of available empirical evidence, distortion of the claims of leading protagonists, or reliance upon examples from the literature which differ from the consensus of the movement but which suit the biases of the critic. (p. 234)

Concluding Remarks

There is a tendency to condemn appropriate technology for all the wrong reasons and regardless of its true intent and focus. Several writers have pointed out that many of the criticisms of appropriate technology have been made in spite of empirical evidence to the contrary (Kaplinsky, 1990; Willoughby, 1990). That said, it must be stated as well that there is also a tendency on the part of some appropriate technology advocates to overstate its role and effectiveness. Unfortunately, this stance sometimes underlies the attitude that appropriate technology is the only acceptable technological approach to Third World development. This seemingly intolerant attitude toward an integrated approach to development problems in the Third World only works to raise suspicion about the motives of some appropriate technologists. Nicholas Jequier did put things in perspective years ago when he wrote:

> *Appropriate technology is not, and should not be viewed as a second-best solution. Conversely, neither should its role be over-estimated: appropriate technology is not a universal substitute for the conventional modern technology. Appropriate and modern technologies are complementary rather than contradictory, and the emphasis given to the former does not and should not rule out the use of the latter in those cases where they are particularly well adapted to local conditions. (Jequier, 1979, p.3)*

However it is interpreted, appropriate technology must be progressive and not retrogressive. Third World countries are advancing in socioeconomic and technological development and must move forward not backward with this progress. Appropriate technology is not meant to be static or promote stagnation but to change as a country achieves progress in its level of development. In the end a new and different kind of appropriate technology with emphasis on environmental sustainability must take precedence as success is realized in the eradication of abject poverty and the reduction of unemployment and inequality.

The need for labor-intensive technology in parts of the Third World in order to adapt to existing circumstances is understandable especially in a situation of scarce capital. However development must proceed beyond adaptation to concern itself with changing these circumstances. Desirable progress is desperately needed in the Third World and cannot be achieved merely by adapting to present conditions. The determinants of technological appropriateness must include an evolutionary capacity factor. This is to say that it is essential "to bring innovators in appropriate technology to think not only in terms of today's needs and resources, but also in terms of building up a system of permanent innovation in appropriate technology" (Jequier, 1979, p. 20). A system of permanent innovation in appropriate technology in the long run should engender domestic capacity to absorb and generate needed capital and technology.

Capital, internally or externally derived, is a necessary factor and must be an essential part of any formula for development in the Third World.

Finally, the establishment of several appropriate technology organizations in recent years is a necessary approach toward the adoption and diffusion of appropriate technology, but must not be the only strategy. A commonly cited obstacle to mass diffusion of appropriate technology is the existing power relations that favor advanced capital-intensive technology. Unless the current economic, political, and social structures that promote large-scale technology are overhauled to ensure a level playing field, the generation and diffusion of appropriate technology would remain sub-optimal at best. This calls for some policy action to remove current incentives that are mostly in favor of capital-intensive technology.

References

Akubue, A. I. (2000, Winter/Spring). Appropriate technology for socioeconomic development in the Third World. Journal of Technology Studies, XXVI(1), 33-43.

Anderson, M. B. (1985). Technology transfer: Implications for women. In C. Overholt, M. B. Anderson, K. Cloud, & J. E. Austin (Eds.), Gender roles in development projects (pp. 57 – 77). West Hartford, CT: Kumarian Press.

Bhatt, V. V. (1980). The development problem, strategy, and technology choice: Sarvodaya and socialist approaches in India. In F. A. Long and A. Oleson (Eds.), Appropriate technology and social values—A critical appraisal (pp. 151 – 175). Cambridge, MA: Ballinger Publishing Company.

Betz, M. J., McGowan, P., & Wigand, R. T. (Eds.). (1984). Appropriate technology: Choices and development. Durham, NC: Duke University Press.

Bourrieres, P. (1979). Adaptation of technologies to available resources. In A. Robinson (Ed.), Appropriate technologies for Third World development (pp. 1 – 7). New York, NY: St. Martin's Press.

Brooks, H. (1980). A critique of the concept of appropriate technology. In F. A. Long and A. Oleson (Eds.), Appropriate technology and social values—A critical appraisal (pp. 53 – 78). Cambridge, MA: Ballinger Publishing Company.

Carley, M. & Christie, I. (1993). Managing sustainable development. Minneapolis, MN: University of Minnesota Press.

Congdon, R. J. (ed.). (1977). Introduction to appropriate technology: Toward a simple life-style. Emmaus, PA: Rodale Press.

Cornish, E. (1979, December). Think small. The Futurist, VIII (6), 276 – 280.

Crittenden, A. (1975, October 26). The economist thinks small. The New York Times, F5.

Darrow, K. & Saxenian, M. (1986). Appropriate technology sourcebook: A guide to practical books for village and small community technology. Stanford, CA: Volunteers in Asia.

Day, G. & Croxton, S. (1993). Appropriate technology, participatory technology, and the environment. Journal of Design History, 6(3), 179179-183.

Dunn, P. D. (1978). Appropriate technology—technology with a human face. New York, NY: Schoken Books.

Evans, D. D. and Alder, N. (Eds.). (1979). Appropriate technology for development: A discussion and case histories. Boulder, CO: Westview Press.

Grieve, R. H. (2004). Appropriate technology in a globalizing world. International Journal of Technology Management and Sustainable Development, 3(3), 173-187.

Harrison, P. (1980). The Third World tomorrow. Harmondsworth: Penguin Books.

Hazeltine, B. & Bull, C. (1999). Appropriate technology: Tools, choices, and implications. San Diego, CA: Academic Press.

Hollick, M. (1982). The appropriate technology movement and its literature: A retrospective. Technology in Society, 4(3), 213 – 229.

Jequier, N. (1976). Appropriate technology: problems and promises. Paris, France: OECD.

Jequier, N. (1979). Appropriate technology: Some criteria. In A. S. Bhalla (Ed.), <u>Towards global action for appropriate technology</u> (pp. 1 – 22). Elmsford, NY: Pergamon Press Inc.

Jequier, N. and Blanc, G. (1983). <u>The world of Appropriate Technology.</u> Paris, France: Organization for Economic Cooperation and Development.

Kaplinsky, R. (1990). <u>The economies of small: Appropriate technology in a changing world</u>. London, England: Intermediate Technology Publications.

Long, F. A. (1980). Introduction. In F. A. Long and A. Oleson (Eds.), <u>Appropriate technology and social values—A critical appraisal</u> (pp. 1 – 8). Cambridge, MA: Ballinger Publishing Company.

Morawetz, D. (1974, September). Employment implications of industrialization in developing countries: A survey. <u>The Economic Journal, 84</u>(333), 491 – 542.

Norwine, J. and Gonzalez, A. (1988). Introduction. In J. Norwine and A. Gonzalez (Eds.), <u>The Third World: States of mind and being</u> (pp. 1 – 5). London, England: Unwin Hyman, Limited.

Pacey, A. (1990). <u>Technology in world civilization: A thousand-year history.</u> Cambridge, MA: The MIT Press.

Pellegrini, U. (1979). The problem of appropriate technology. In A. De Giorgio and C. Roveda (Eds.), <u>Criteria for selecting appropriate technologies under different cultural, technical and social conditions</u> (pp. 1 – 5). New York, NY: Pergamon Press.

Perkins, D. H. (1980). China's experience with rural small-scale industry. In F. A. Long and A. Oleson (Eds.), <u>Appropriate technology and social values—A critical appraisal</u> (pp. 177 – 192). Cambridge, MA: Ballinger Publishing Company.

Practical Action (2007). Practical Action is the new name of ITDG, Retrieved 2008 from: http://practicalaction.org/print.php?id=practicalaction

Reddy, A. K. (1979). Problems in the generation of appropriate technologies. In A. Robinson (Ed.), <u>Appropriate technologies for Third World development</u> (pp. 173-189).New York: St. Martin's Press

Riskin, C. (1979). Intermediate technology in China's rural development. In A. Robinson (Ed.), <u>Appropriate technologies for Third World development</u> (pp. 52 – 74). New York, NY: St. Martin's Press.

Robinson, A. (1979). Introduction. In A. Robinson (Ed.), <u>Appropriate technologies for Third World development</u> (pp. xi – xix). New York, NY: St. Martin's Press.

Rosenbrock, H. H. (1979). The redirection of technology. In A. De Giorgio and C. Roveda (Eds.), <u>Criteria for selecting appropriate technologies under different cultural, technical and social conditions</u> (pp. 7 – 13). New York, NY: Pergamon Press.

Sampat, P. (1995). India's low-tech energy success. <u>World Watch</u>, 8(6), 21-23.

Schumacher, E. F. (1973). <u>Small is beautiful: Economics as if people mattered</u>. New York, NY: Harper & Row, Publishers.

Schumacher, E. F. (1974, December). Economics should begin with people not goods. <u>The Futurist,</u> VIII(6), 274 – 275.

Singer, H. (1985). Appropriate technology and basic-needs strategy. In M. Carr (Ed.), <u>The AT reader: Theory and practice in</u>

appropriate technology (pp. 27 – 28). Croton-on-Hudson, NY

Stewart, F. (1985). Underdeveloped technology? In M. Carr (Ed.), The AT reader: Theory and practice in appropriate technology (pp. 27 – 28). Croton-on-Hudson, NY: Intermediate Technology Development Group of North America.

Toffler, A. (1980). The third wave. New York, NY: William Morrow and Company, Inc.

Thormann, P. (1979). Proposal for a program in appropriate technology. In A. Robinson (Ed.), Appropriate technologies for Third World development (pp. 280 – 299). New York, NY: St. Martin's Press.

Willoughby, K. W. (1990). Technology choice: A critique of the Appropriate Technology Movement. Boulder, CO: Westview Press.

Chapter SEVEN

Technology, Development, and Gender Disparity in the Third World

Introduction

In what seems a recurring observation in its annual Human Development Reports, the United Nations Development Program (UNDP) notes that the human progress that developing countries achieved in a period of three decades took the industrialized countries a century to attain. People are living longer, infant mortality rates and illiteracy rates have declined significantly, and appreciable improvements in basic-needs fulfillment of citizens have been realized. According to the World Bank (2001),

> In the past four decades life expectancy in the developing world increased 20 years on average, the infant mortality rate fell more than half, and fertility rates declined by almost half. In the past two decades net primary school enrollment in developing countries increased by 13 percent. Between 1965 and 1998 average incomes more than doubled in developing countries, and in 1990-1998 alone the number of people in extreme poverty fell by 78 million. (pp. v-vi)

A troubling concern, however, is the notion that gains from technological and socioeconomic development have not been equally beneficial to the genders. Males tend to be better off in most cases, often capturing a disproportionate share of the proceeds of progress than females. There is much evidence in support of the claim that women are in the majority of the poor in the Third World today. According to the UNDP (1995), 70% of an estimated 1.3 billion people living in poverty worldwide are women, most of them living in developing countries. However, the feminization of poverty is not so much about more women than men being poor, but about the "severity of poverty and the greater hardship women face in lifting themselves and their children out of the trap" (UNDP, 1997, p. 64). This differential gender impact underlies the UNDP (1997) statement that "for too long it was assumed that development was a process that lifts all boats, that its benefits trickled down to all income classes and that it was gender neutral in its impact; experience teaches otherwise" (p. 1).

This chapter is about Third World women in relation to technological and socioeconomic progress. It examines the differential gender outcome of this progress and probable causes. Nzewi (1996) attributed obstacles to women engaging in and pursuing careers in science, technology, engineering, and mathematics (STEM) to factors of tradition and cultural norms, attitudes and prejudices, religion, poverty, and ignorance. Despite the progress made over the past 50 years in establishing legal recognition of the inalienable human rights of women, "they are still mired in traditional practice discouraging their de facto equality" (Frey, 2004, p. 14). Inherent in the socialization process of societies is a particularly damaging depiction of gender roles as biological rather than social constructs. The power of the socialization process in inhibiting women's education in science, engineering, mathematics, and technology education is often underestimated and has not received the attention it deserves among professionals in the field. The view espoused in this article is that this indoctrination inspires phobia, diffidence, and lack of interest among girls and women, who tend to believe that some academic disciplines and professional careers are beyond their abilities. This mindset is a powerful force that is contributing to the perpetuation of poverty among Third World women in particular and the Third World in general. Logic provides that peace cannot endure where poverty prevails, and that the poor would migrate toward relief if relief does not come to them.

Some Background

Investigations into women's issues in relation to technological, social, and economic progress have been relatively recent, but rural women have for years been affected one way or the other by modern technology and development. Women and girls in Third World societies are more likely than men and boys to have less access to technology, education, technical training, land, credit, and basic needs. Historically, women have performed mostly laborious, gender-assigned duties with the knowledge, techniques, skills, and tools passed down from generation to generation. The duties of Third World women can be placed into three categories: reproductive and nurturing, family and household management, and productive and/or income-generating roles (Momsen, 1998; UNDP, 1997). Studies have shown that in developing countries women, especially poor women, work an average of 12 to 18 hours a day compared to an average of 8 to 12 hours a day for men (Jacobson, 1993; Momsen, 1998). Among the tasks women perform are subsistence farming, food production and processing, traditional weaving and sewing, soap-making, petty trading, craft-making, baking, shop-keeping, procuring energy fuel and water, household work, payment of children's school fees, animal care, caring for the elderly, and raising children (Akubue, 1995).

Women's Access to Productive Resources

Centuries of tradition in many developing countries define women's roles.

The gap between male and female literacy rates in the Third World has been narrowing, although female illiteracy continues to be higher than male illiteracy. Out of an estimated 840 million illiterate adults in the developing world, 538 million of them are women. The female illiteracy rate stands at about 39% in contrast with a male illiteracy rate of 21% (Momsen, 1998; UNDP, 1997). Women and girls tend to receive less education and training than men and boys in most Third World societies (Herz, 1989). This is not surprising because in the absence or poor enforcement of legislation on compulsory education for all children, coupled with the tendency to value sons over daughters, girls are less likely than boys to go to school. Investments in education continue to be higher for sons than for daughters. This is in spite of studies showing that the education of girls tends to produce far-reaching socioeconomic benefits for the girls and women themselves, their families, and the society in general (Bellew, Raney, & Subbarao, 1992; de Vries, 1971; Hadden & London, 1996; Herz, 1989; Summers, 1992). Indeed, most studies have revealed that when schools open their doors wider to girls and women, as well as boys and men, the benefits multiply. According to the United Nations International Children Emergency Fund (UNICEF, 1994),

> *The education of girls is one of the most important investments that any developing country can make in its own future. In the long term, almost every other aspect of progress, from nutrition to family planning, from child health to women's rights, is profoundly affected by whether or not a nation educates its girls. (p. 20)*

In fact, several years ago, Dr. J. E. Aggrey, an eminent educator from Ghana, observed that "if you educate a man, you simply educate an individual, but if you educate a woman, you educate a family" (Topouzis, 1990, p. 62). Among the short-term benefits of educating girls and women are smaller families, better spacing of births, healthier children, less economic dependence, and less vulnerability to abusive spouses. "These initial gains seem also to be readily translated into a range of longer-term benefits that include longer life expectancy, declines in overall mortality rates, and improvements in both social and economic development rates" (Hadden & London, 1996, p. 43).

Increasingly, parents in Third World societies are realizing the importance of educating their daughters, but there are still some impediments. Not only are more illiterate women than there are illiterate, but also two thirds of the children not enrolled in school are girls Momsen (1998).

As much as women would like to participate in adult literacy programs, their incredible responsibilities and workloads keep them from taking advantage of opportunities. The persistence of poverty among many families also works against the education of girls and women. Due mostly to hardship in poor households, girls are more likely than boys to stay at home to help their mothers with income-earning efforts and other household chores. "In fact, the increasing tendency in many areas of keeping girls out of school to help with their mothers' work virtually ensures that another generation of females will grow up with poorer prospects than their brothers" (Jacobson 1993, p. 75). The concern for the safety of daughters is another critical factor in the decision whether to send girls to school. Their vulnerability, the fear of becoming victims of rape, and a strong taboo on pregnancy out of wedlock are reasons to shield girls from the vagaries of life outside the home. Once in 1991 in a Kenyan boarding school, for example, 71 teen-aged schoolgirls were raped by their male classmates and 19 of them died. The school's principal, a woman, sadly defended the rapists by suggesting that 'the boys never meant any harm against the girls, they just wanted to rape' (Frey, 2004). In some societies, parents see educating girls as an exercise in futility since they are given away in marriage and the reward of years of education may elude the natal family. Lastly, the impact of colonial perspectives on gender roles continues to influence gender educational opportunities. As Charlton (1984) pointed out,

> The actual content of many home economics projects and programs remains solidly housework-based, a result of the success of the Western stereotype of women as domestic, which has been incorporated into the expanding education system in Third World countries since the Second World War. (p. 163)

This curriculum design does not, for instance, help women improve their capabilities as farmers. The curriculum is, however, sustained on the premise that humanity would be best served if women could "improve the way in which they cared for their children and catered for the family needs. As a result family welfare programs were devised which gave women instruction in home economics, in improved nutrition, health, and hygiene" (Young, 1993, 19). Yet, women play an indispensable role in food production and processing in Third World countries. For example, women in Africa produce 80% of domestically consumed food, 70 to 80% of food crops grown on the Indian sub-continent and about 50% in Latin America and the Caribbean (Jacobson, 1993; Momsen, 1998). Estimates from Kenya suggest that providing women with the same access to factors and inputs as men would increase the value of their output nearly 22% (World Bank, 2000). It is difficult to argue with the statement by de Vries (1971) that the "failure of many communities to train women, as well as men, in the newer agricultural methods being introduced may be a contributing factor to gradual reduction in the relative productivity of women" (p. 7).

The agricultural extension service is overwhelmingly a male-dominated profession in the Third World; only 13% of the agents in the late 1980s and early 1990s were women. In the continent of Africa and India, the statistics were as meager as 7% and 0.5%, respectively (UNDP, 1995). Trained and equipped usually in urban environments still laden with vestiges of colonialism, male extension agents are, not surprisingly, partial to men, even in areas where women are responsible for major cash or food crop production. A study of the pattern of visits by extension workers to farmers in Kenya showed that 49% of the female-operated farms were never visited by an agent in contrast with only 28% of male or jointly operated farms (Momsen, 1998). The gender bias against women is further compounded by cultural and religious practices that prohibit direct contact between women and male strangers/extension agents (Akubue, 1995; Young, 1993). Moreover, with a ratio of one extension agent to 2,000 or 3,000 farmers, extension systems in many Third World countries are severely constrained and understandably cannot meet the overwhelming demand for their services. The situation is quite the opposite in Europe and North America, where one extension agent serves 300 to 400 farmers (Quisumbing, 1998). Under this condition, it is often assumed that husbands would pass information on to their wives from extension service workers. Studies in Asia, Africa, and Latin America and the Caribbean, however, show that such information communicated indirectly is often distorted and less accurate (Akubue, 1995). According to studies in Kenya, "women farmers generally adopt the advice given by extension agents; where they do not, the principal reason they cite are lack of credit and income to buy inputs, and lack of enough land" (Herz, 1989, p. 44).

Generally, rural financial institutions still prefer and require land title as collateral for loan extension in many Third World countries. This requirement tends to be partial to male borrowers, since land ownership and title in most cases belong to men (Akubue, 1991). "In the patrilineal cultures found in Bangladesh, India, Pakistan, much of sub-Saharan Africa, and Latin America, women gain access to land only through their husbands or sons" (Jacobson, 1993, p. 70). This has not always been the traditional system of land tenure in the Third World. The current system is very much the result of European views of what constitutes gender-appropriate roles, which replaced a precolonial system of communal land ownership. To implement the new system, colonial administrations registered communal land and made land titles out in men's names (Momsen, 1991; Quisumbing, 1998; Tinker, 1981; Young, 1993;). Contemporary Third World development professionals have tacitly endorsed past actions by maintaining the status quo. For most rural women, access to land is usually in the form of user rights rather than absolute ownership rights (Quisumbing, Brown, Feldstein, Haddad, & Pena, 1995). In instances where women have ownership rights, their share is usually small relative to men's. Lacking outright land ownership and land title commonly required by banks for loan extension almost guarantees lack of funding for the women. The traditional moneylenders' practice of charging usury rates is an exorbitant and exploitative alternative source of credit. Without a propitious rural financial market to count on, women have difficulty mobilizing enough start-up capital for new businesses or expanding existing undertakings. Women, like men, need credit to acquire essential appropriate technology, tools, and material input to improve productivity, profits, and standard of living. Not surprisingly, the cumulative effects of protracted denial of women's access to productive resources, education, and training -a concomitant of gender bias-are worsening gender disparity and inequity.

The Impact of Technological, Social, and Economic Development on Women

Not having as much access as men inhibits rural women's technological literacy and, definitely, their motor, cognitive, and interpersonal communication skills. As a result, women lack the skills required to perform in modern industry and agriculture. Modern production technology requires new skills and specialization that are vastly different from the traditional skills these women possess. Consequently, some researchers have contended that the "most common result of 'development' is to relegate women to the subsistence sector in agriculture and low-paying jobs in manufacturing and industry" (Tadesse, 1982, p. 79).

Women in Manufacturing & Industry

Technological development in the modern industrial sector unmistakably has opened up diverse job opportunities for Third World women. However, questions have been raised about the quality of the jobs thus created. These have been mostly low-wage, low-skill, dead-end jobs where they are easily dispensable. Lacking the necessary skills and specialization, women workers in modern sector factories are mostly "engaged in non-technological gathering, assembling, arranging and packaging activities and therefore technical skills are not being transferred equally to men and women" (Srinivasan, 1981, p. 91).

Regardless of what they are called, maquiladoras in Mexico or export processing zones (EPZs) elsewhere in Latin America, Africa, and Asia, they are industrial plants owned or subcontracted by multinational corporations with headquarters in the industrialized nations. They are export-oriented assembly and manufacturing firms producing goods primarily for re-export to Europe and North America. The location of the industrial plants in the Third World is often a function of cheap labor and profit maximization. These industrial plants, predominantly electronics, textiles, apparel, and footwear industries, hire mostly female labor (Akubue, 1995; Momsen, 1998). It is claimed that women have a number of attributes that are not commonly exhibited by men. Women are said to be nimble-fingered, dexterous, docile, patient, and obedient, and to possess better attention spans than men do. Interestingly, these fine characteristics have contributed significantly to women's vulnerability in the maquiladoras or EPZs. As manufacturing with laborsaving, capital-intensive technology has grown in the maquiladoras and EPZs, the traditional labor-intensive assembly for which they are known no longer enjoys the monopoly it once did, and the characteristic female labor dominance is on the wane. For example, the percentage of female workers in the Mexican maquiladoras fell from a 1982 figure of 77% to 61% in 1990 (Wilson, 1992). Also, cases of sexual harassment and molestation, as well as inhumane and unhealthy working conditions, are not uncommon at these enterprises (Kelly, 1983; Pena, 1997). Mitter (1995) conceded that jobs in the factories are not perfect, but argued that the "conditions of employment are superior to alternatives that women are likely to find as domestic workers, prostitutes, or as workers in the informal sector" (p. 23). This assertion is reasonable but only to the degree that one believes that half a loaf of bread is better than no bread at all. Utilizing women to the extent of their potential in all spheres of life is not a matter of doing them a favor, but engaging the enormous human resource of one half of humanity for the betterment of communities and nations. A study of women workers in the Dominican Republic shows that they are usually fired when they fail to meet increasing output quotas, get married, or become pregnant (Momsen, 1998). Paradoxically, the so-called advantages of the female gender have merely served to congregate women at the lower rungs of the organizational ladder.

Certain policy actions by Third World governments have not and are not helping women's cause in the least. In their desperate bid to attract multinational corporations to locate plants in the modern sector of their countries, some governments offer them incentives-some of which compound women's socioeconomic problems. Incentives such as promising a disciplined workforce and repression of union activities are common. The concentration of the industrial plants in the modern sector and cuts in social programs to comply with structural adjustment programs (SAPs) of the International Monetary Fund (IMF) and the World Bank ensure a steady flow of unskilled female labor from the traditional sector (Akubue, 1995; Momsen, 1998). Budget cuts in education, health care, nutrition programs, and agricultural extension services have forced rural women from the grip of village patriarchy into the control of industrial patriarchy. The austerity measures in Third World countries that have adopted SAPs have exacerbated existing gender disparity and marginalization of women (McAfee, 1990; Topouzis, 1990). The situation is not much different for women in the mechanized agricultural sector.

Women in the Agricultural Sector

It is not unusual for the introduction of a new farm technology to result in radical shifts in gender roles in agricultural labor. Anderson (1985) stated that "when a technology is introduced, those who either already enjoy higher status or who are in a position to corner it may move into tasks that were previously low status when done without the benefit of the new technology" (p. 61). Since men are more likely than women to have access to technology and associated technical training, any shifts in sex roles due to new agricultural technologies would tend to favor mostly men. Momsen (1991) argued similarly that the "introduction of a new tool may cause a particular job to be reassigned to the opposite sex and men tend to assume tasks that become mechanized" (p. 50). Thus the introduction of post-harvest food processing technologies may mean the loss of a traditional source of income for rural poor and landless women. For example, women who depend on the traditional hand pounding with mortar and pestle to de-husk rice or grain as hired labor may lose their job as a result to rice, corn, or oil mills operated by men. This is especially the case in Africa and Asia, where many women fit into this category of hired rural labor (Momsen, 1991; Quisumbing et al, 1995). In rural West Africa, hired female labor processed palm nuts and kernels for the extraction of widely consumed palm oil. Most of these women lost their jobs with the introduction of oil mills operated by men. Still, for Moslem women restricted by purdah from work outside the homestead and in the company of men, technology-induced relocation of the workplace to the mills may mean the loss of a vital source of income. Furthermore, while male landowners in Africa and elsewhere experienced lightened workload and expansion in cash crop cultivation with modern tractors and improved animal-powered farm equipment, work for their wives increased, with more area to weed, hoe, and plant (Jacobson, 1993). A study of a Tiv farm development project in Nigeria showed that women experienced "a disproportionately high share of the labor increase without a corresponding increase in income; female labor requirements rose by 17%, while those of men rose by only 6%" (Young, 1993, p. #52). These conditions for women simply cannot be dismissed as fortuitous and without connection to existing power relations and decision-making processes in the Third World.

Decision Making in the Third World

It appears from the above that technology and development have actually been contributing to widening the gender gap instead of reducing it. The general image of technological and socioeconomic development is and has been that of a male directed and controlled process. Seen as such, development has commonly been viewed as a process that is structured by men and for men, and women are expected to abide without questions. The literature is replete with evidence that women are often not involved or consulted in the planning and designing of technology-based development projects and programs with direct impact on them. For instance, projects involving solar cookers in India, hydraulic palm oil presses in Nigeria, and high yield variety maize in Mexico were implemented with little input from women who are and have traditionally been responsible for cooking and palm oil processing. The introduction of solar cookers in India, Kenya, and elsewhere seems expedient given the serious problems of deforestation and fuelwood scarcity. As logical as this innovation seemed, rural women resisted it mainly because of their labor patterns, food habits, and the intermittent nature of the sun. For instance, women cook the main meal of the day when they return from the farms in the evening. The solar cooker is not very useful at sunset, and it is highly unlikely that some women would readily abandon established labor patterns in the village to accommodate a new technology. Furthermore, since the solar cooker must face directly into the sun to be effective, it requires constant relocation to track the sun as it changes positions. This is inconvenient to say the least. Finally, even though some governments subsidize the cost of solar cookers as in India for instance, the price remained prohibitive for a large number of people (Blankenberg, 1991).

The problems with the introduction of the solar cooker and similar schemes elsewhere were due mostly to flaws in the planning process. As appropriate as the innovations seemed, their planning and introduction lacked the valuable input of the women who are the majority of the target end-users. This mistake is often perpetuated by the erroneous assumption that men who dominate the decision-making process know what women need. The importance of listening to women articulate their needs and including them in decision making cannot be overemphasized. An Indian adage teaches us that "As a bird cannot fly on one wing, no society can make progress unless its women too join men in all activities" (Bhattacharya & Bose, 1995, p. 93). Science and technology have become the most potent sources of change and empowerment in modern society. To insist on the age-old practice of excluding women in decisions concerning their development is to be unwise and myopic. For technology to be advantageous rather than disadvantageous to women in its role as a productive resource, Charlton (1984) suggested, as has this author, that

> women must have the means to communicate their needs and preferences, and they must be informed of available alternatives. In short, women must participate in the decision making about new technologies. From a practical standpoint, this means that there must be much greater female involvement in the institutions that serve to transfer technology: government agencies, including extension services; private development organizations, and profit-making companies. (p. 101)

Women are conspicuously underrepresented in decision and policy making concerning technological and socioeconomic development. Explaining the reason for this condition, Young (1993) suggested plausibly that development practitioners are cautious not to violate what may be strongly regarded cultural practices and values. Mostly male-dominated government officials from the Third World often claim that concerns about the absence of women at high levels of government and their lack of active involvement in policy making is a Western preoccupation of no interest even to their women. The few women in positions of power and authority are being lost through attrition as many of them experience first-hand what it entails to be "lonely at the top." However, efforts to improve the status of women and to enlist their self-confidence, intellectual, and decision-making capabilities for the benefit of society have culminated in landmark conferences and policy adjustments worldwide.

Confronting Gender Bias against Women

As a result of concerted efforts in recent decades, the plight of women in general is a topic of serious research, discourse, and action worldwide. Various governments are cooperating with international agencies to initiate gender sensitive policies and programs. For instance, in 1973, the US Congress adopted the Percy Amendment (Section 113 of the 1973 Foreign Assistance Act) sponsored by Republican Senator William Percy (retired) of Illinois. As the amendment requires, US bilateral development assistance "shall be administered so as to give particular attention to those programs, projects and activities which tend to integrate women into the national economies of foreign countries, thus improving their status and assisting the total development effort" (Blumberg, 1990, p. 2). The amendment also directed the US Agency for International Development (AID) to include the likely effects of development projects on women in its feasibility studies of projects. The Women in Development (WID) Office of the AID was established in direct response to this amendment. The office assists in the preparation and testing of case studies involving projects funded by the AID. This legislation was unprecedented in its strong endorsement of women

as contributors and agents of economic development as well as its beneficiaries. Planners, therefore, must guard against the negative effects of their projects on women and focus on the need to enhance women's productivity, raise their income, and promote their access to economically productive resources as a means to achieving overall national economic growth. (Overholt, Anderson, Cloud, & Austin, 1985, p. 11)

Similar efforts followed the US example. The British Commonwealth, for example, in 1980 established a Women and Development (WAD) program that received the endorsement of all of its member nations (Momsen, 1991). Third World governments have also initiated pragmatic educational reforms that are having positive impact on their literacy rates. More girls and young women are enrolling in schools today than ever before. The combined female primary and secondary enrollment in the developing world jumped dramatically from 38% in 1970 to 68% in 1992 (UNDP, 1995).

Not only have national governments taken direct action to mitigate gender disparity, they are also contributing to the gender work of the United Nations (UN). Under the initiative and auspices of the UN Commission on the Status of Women, established in 1946 by the UN Economic and Social Council, 1975 was designated International Women's Year. The commission initiates and oversees programs and activities aimed at promoting equal rights between the sexes. In keeping with this mandate, the commission deals with issues related to women's participation in political life and in decision making, and women's role in and contribution to development. The adoption of the Declaration on the Elimination of Violence against Women by the UN General Assembly in 1993 is credited to the commission's work on violence against women.

The World conferences on women held in Mexico City, Mexico, in 1975; Copenhagen, Denmark, in 1980; Nairobi, Kenya, in 1985; and Beijing, China, in 1995 have kept attention focused on the condition of women and produced action plans for improving women's status worldwide (Kaye, 1995; Young, 1993). The UN Decade for Women, from 1976 to 1985, started with the creation by the UN General Assembly of a Voluntary Fund for the decade that became known as the UN Fund for Women (UNIFEM). UNIFEM's efforts are focused on three areas: strengthening women's economic capacity as entrepreneurs and producers, promoting governance and leadership that increase women's participation in decision-making processes that shape their lives, and promoting women's human rights (UNIFEM, 1998).

Tibetan Women from exile gag themselves with silk scarves given by China to guests at the FWCW opening ceremonies and stage a silent vigil in pouring rain on the second day of the NGO Forum, to symbolize China's silencing of Tibetan women's voices.
Photo courtesy of Carole Samdup, CTC

The 1975 conference in Mexico adopted the World Plan of Action (WPA) from the UN. The WPA is a compendium of objectives encompassing priority issues such as enabling "educational opportunities for

154

women, better employment prospects, equality in political and social participation, and increased welfare services" (Young, 1993, p. 25). The subsequent conferences in Copenhagen, Nairobi, and Beijing have been vital to review work in progress, evaluate accomplishments and challenges, pass important resolutions, and develop follow-up action plans. Professional associations also work cooperatively with the UN for gender equality and equity. For instance, the Gender and science and Technology Association (GASAT), has through their conferences worked toward narrowing the gender gap in relation to increasing female presence in the fields of science and technology education. GASAT made vital contributions towards the inclusion of science and technology in the Platform of Action during the last UN conference on women held in Beijing, China (GASAT, 1998). This document chronicled "12 Critical Areas of Concern" about women that must be addressed as a matter of urgency: poverty, education, health, violence, armed conflict, the economy, power and decision-making, mechanisms for women's advancement, women's human rights, mass media, the environment, and the female child (Frey, 2004).

Experiences garnered from these conferences have been invaluable in promoting attitude and policy changes in governments and international agencies. For instance, under pressure to develop a measure of progress that transcends per capita income, the UNDP has developed complementary gender-related indices to its still controversial Human Development Index (HDI). The 1995 Human Development Report introduced the Gender-related Development Index (GDI) and the Gender Empowerment Measure (GEM), specifically for monitoring gender disparity. The GDI is an adjusted variant of the HDI intended to measure gender inequality in basic capabilities. For instance, "if a nation's women are doing worse than its men in earnings, education, or life expectancy, the country will have a lower GDI than HDI" (Forcione & Breslow, 1995, p. 43). The GEMD also measures gender inequality but in the key equally weighted areas of women's job status, political status, and income status (Forcione & Breslow, 1995). In other words, the GEM is concerned with gender economic and political participation and decision making. High GEM statistics indicate that the countries involved "are not only good at strengthening the basic capabilities of women, they have also opened many opportunities for them to participate in economic and political fields" (UNDP, 1997, p. 41). All this has been impressive, but it goes without saying that this concerted effort to improve the status of women must continue without abatement, for there is much more yet to be done.

Work to be done and Some Suggestions

Women's positions in most contemporary social institutions in Third World countries continue to be subordinate in many cases and border on tokenism in others. A thorough examination of the cultural and political milieu in educational systems and the workplace is imperative to identify and isolate factors that work against women's enrollment and success in technological fields and their upward mobility in public and private organizations. Any attempt to improve the enrollment of women in fields such as technology education, engineering, and science where they are poorly represented must start with attempts to identify and remove impediments keeping them out of these disciplines. Changes in institutional cultures, societal power relations, social values, and stereotypes are inevitable in this effort. Successfully identified, information about results must be widely disseminated and factored into all future program design and development.

The dissemination of information is crucial and cannot be overlooked in the effort to eradicate gender disparity and improve the status of women in general. Information dissemination will not only reduce the common practice of reinventing the wheel, but will also speed up the adaptation and replication of successful programs as appropriate in different locations. Due primarily to extensive publicity, highly successful Rotating Savings and Credit Associations (ROSCAs) such as the Grameen Bank of Bangladesh, which provide micro loans to rural women, are increasing in number and have been very effective in empowering women (Akubue, 1991). ROSCAs have enabled rural women, denied loans from conventional financial institutions for lack of collateral and track records, to purchase low-cost appropriate technologies for new businesses or to expand existing ones. Looms, hand-sewing machines, improved cooking stoves, hand grinders, manual typewriters, solar cookers, photovoltaic cells, hand tools, and biogas digesters producing gas used in electric lighting, water pumping, and cooking are some examples of appropriate technologies purchased with loans from ROSCAs.

Programs in Mexico and Jamaica, for instance, teach young, unemployed, low-income women technical skills for jobs traditionally associated with the male gender. With assistance from UNIFEM, 10 women from Tempoal in Mexico started a thriving manufacturing enterprise after receiving training as welders and machinists in Colombia, South America. The women started a company to manufacture simple, easily affordable water pumps for export and domestic sale in Mexico. In the Caribbean island of Jamaica, a skill-developing training program that prepares women for careers in the construction industry is known for its high job placement rates (Antrobus & Rogers, 1980; Dorman, 1991; McLeod, 1986). A successful barefoot college in Tilonia, a village in the Indian state of Rajasthan, provides night schools in villages and offers education that is suitable for rural life. The campus administration promotes the participation of peasants in their own development, which is in keeping with Mahatma Gandhi's philosophy of empowering village people. The priority of the college is to address problems of drinking water, girl education, health and sanitation, rural unemployment, income generation, electricity and power, social awareness and ecological preservation. The 5 principles of which the college was founded are: equality, collectivity, self-reliance, decentralization, and austerity. Since its inception in 1972 by its founder, Sanjit Bunker Roy, the college has trained "two generations of villagers without any formal paper qualifications to become health-care workers, solar engineers, hand-pump mechanics, and teachers in their communities" (Misra, 2000, 1). The college uses solar-powered electricity for power source and passive solar energy for heating and cooling. The success of these programs is a strong testimony that gender roles are primarily social constructs as opposed to indelible biological impositions. Associations such as Gender and Science and Technology (GASAT) remain unwavering in their belief that given a level playing field, women are quite capable of mastering the skills for careers in science, technology, and mathematics.

However, more extensive improvements in gender equality are possible if the replication of successful projects is executed in tandem with other strategies. Famous professional women can be enlisted as role models in a multifaceted strategy especially to inspire young women to pursue academic education and careers in traditionally male-dominated fields such as technology education, engineering, and computer science. Even in the United States where parity in literacy rates has been achieved between the genders, women still constitute a very small percentage of students graduating with bachelor's degrees in engineering and computer science. Only 9% and 29% of students who earn bachelor's degrees in engineering and computer science, respectively, are women (Rengel, 2000). Using famous women engineers, technologists, and scientists as role models, young women can be encouraged to enroll in related majors. For instance, Sarah Akbar of Kuwait Oil Company was a petroleum engineer and a member of the Kuwaiti team of firefighters who fought the inferno at Kuwait oil wells when operation Desert Storm ended in 1991. Sarah was the first woman ever in Kuwait and in the Middle East to participate in a potentially hazardous task of that kind. The publicity that followed Sarah's bravura turned her into a role model, symbol of equality, and mentor for young Kuwaiti women. A study at Kuwait University later showed that the number of women enrolled in petroleum engineering increased substantially since Sarah's unprecedented feat (Soliman, 1993). Sarah's efforts were a lesson in self-confidence, courage, and risk-taking for women, and another refutation of the theory that we are born with naturally assigned, not to speak of unchangeable, gender roles. However, to be effective, the task of collecting and making this and other successful schemes available for dissemination must be the responsibility of a central body established and supported by governments in the Third World.

Centers for the collection and dissemination of information on effective strategies for improving women's status and achieving gender equality have been set up in many Third World countries in recent years. Women's bureaus "collate, collect and coordinate existing information as well as encourage, fund and partially direct future research" (Nelson, 1981, p. 49). The charge of most women's bureaus is not only to ensure that women play a greater, and important, part in all development projects, but also to plan, coordinate, and monitor a wide variety of other projects having to do with women. To this end, women's bureaus act as catalysts integrating women into male-dominated areas such as the agricultural extension profession. Making sure that women are recruited and trained includes educating male colleagues on respect for and sensitivity to issues concerning women. Women's bureaus and similar agencies are definitely a welcome idea, but they can be subverted by inadequate funding, lack of trained personnel, and having little or no political clout. According to Young (1993), many of these agencies have not been very effective for these reasons.

Finally, socialization in traditional societies often includes risk aversion for women. The march toward gender equality will be better served with strategies that assist women to unlearn years of belief that risk-taking is improper for the female gender. Being able to give up what one "is" for what one "could become" is the essence of risk-taking. Women are by tradition and mores more likely than men to avoid taking risks for fear of failing. It is important to point out here that failure is itself an important aspect of the learning process. Properly managed, failure can be a positive guide to success.

Concluding Remarks

Women's input and participation in global affairs have been limited and constrained by traditions, power relations, and norms of behavior existing in most communities. This social structure falsely legitimizes and reinforces women's subordinate position, economically and socially, both in the household and in the larger society. To paraphrase Fatima Mernissi, as quoted in Mitter (1995), our consciousness at home and at work is the product of our tradition and heritage; the hope lies in freeing ourselves from the myth of an unchanging tradition. These social impediments, coupled with the damaging effects of depicting gender roles as a natural consequence of the biological difference between the genders, account extensively for the present shortage of women globally in fields such as technology education, engineering, science, mathematics, and computer science.

The operating model of technological and socioeconomic development has done little or nothing to change these age-old social norms, values, customs, and traditions as a precondition to women's full and equal partnership. Policy makers, the "architects of development," take a very generic view of technological and socioeconomic transformation, and fail to give due consideration to their possible positive or adverse impact on women's social status. The result "has been that the processes of technological transformation and economic development have only strengthened the pre-existing institutional arrangements, keeping the women as an economically deprived, socially subjugated and politically powerless group" (Roy, 1995, p. 34). The notion of doing things for instead of with women, the result of the social and cultural orientation in most communities, presents a problem in that it denies them the chance to acquire vital knowledge and contacts. To sincerely work toward a society of gender equality and equity, women have to have access to political and economic networks. Speeches and reports that extol the benefits of gender equality are nothing more than empty rhetoric if they are not followed up with commensurate action. As Jacobson (1993) aptly remarked, "development strategies that limit the ability of women to achieve their real human potential are also strategies that limit the potential of communities and nations" (p. 76). Those of us in science and technology need to become involved through scholarly papers and presentations to lend credibility and a sense of urgency to the plight of Third World women and girls. In a "shrinking" world made possible through advances in transportation and communications technology, regional problems tend to quickly extend beyond regional boundaries.

References

Akubue, A. I. (1991). Credit for small-scale rural entrepreneurs in the Third World. International Third World Studies & Review, 3(2), 251-255.

Akubue, A. I. (1995). Technology, women, and development. The Technology Teacher, 55(2), 10-15.

Akubue, A. I. (2001). Gender disparity in Third World technological, social, and economic development. The Journal of Technology Studies, XXVII (2), 64-73.

Anderson, M. B. (1985). Technology transfer: Implications for women. In C. Overholt, M. B. Anderson, K. Cloud, & J. E. Austin (Eds.), Gender roles in development projects (pp. 57-78). West Hartford, CT: Kumarian Press.

Antrobus, P., & Rogers, B. (1980). Hanover street: An experiment to train women in welding and carpentry. New York: Seeds.

Bellew, R., Raney, L., & Subbarao, K. (1992, March). Educating girls. Finance and Development, pp. 54-56.

Bhattacharya, B., & Bose, P. (1995). Role of education and literacy in the development of rural women with special reference to Himalayan region. In A. Bahuguna (Ed.), Science and technology in relation to rural women (pp. 93 – 99). New Delhi, India: Har-Anand.

Blankenberg, F. P. (1991). Appropriate technology for rural development in India. New Delhi, India: Concept.

Blumberg, R. L. (1990, November). Gender matters: Involving women in development in Latin America and the Caribbean (Report No. 70328). Washington, DC: Agency for International Development.

Charlton, S. E. M. (1984). Women in Third World development. Boulder, CO: Westview Press.

de Vries, M. G. (1971). Women, jobs, and development. Finance & Development, 8(4), 2-9.

Dorman, J. (1991). Profiles in progress: Working women. Bridgeport, CT: Discovery Channel

Frey, B. (2004, January). Pervasive violence against women at home and abroad: Sexual violence weapon of control against women around the world. St. Cloud Unabridged, 8 (4), pp. 1, 14, & 15.

Forcione, C., & Breslow, M. (1995). Measuring women's progress. Dollars and Sense, 202, 43.

Gender and Science and Technology Association (1998). Ninth international conference on gender and science and technology. GASAT, www.gustavus.edu/~simpson/gasat/GASAT-9/img001.htm, p. 1.

Hadden, K., & London, B. (1996). Educating girls in the Third World: The demographic, basic needs, and economic benefits. International Journal of Comparative Sociology, 37(1-2), 31-46.

Herz, B. (1989). Women in development: Kenya's experience. Finance and Development, 26(2), 43-45.

Jacobson, J. L. (1993). Changing the gender gap in development. In L. Starke (Ed.), The state of the world (pp. 61-79). New York: Norton.

Kaye, L. (1995, September). To bear the burden. Far Eastern Economic Review, pp. 42-43.

Kelly, M. P. F. (1983). Gender and industry on Mexico's new frontier. In J. Zimmerman (Ed.), The technological woman interfacing with tomorrow (pp. 18-29). New York: Praeger.

McAfee, K. (1990). Why the Third World goes hungry: Selling cheap and buying dear. Commonweal, 117(12), 380-385.

McLeod, R. (1986). The women's construction collective: Building for the future (Issue Brief No. 9). New York: Seeds.

Misra, N. (2000). India's barefoot college generation. The Courier. Retrieved September 4, 2005: http://www.unesco.org/courier/2000_03/uk/dossier/txt02.htm.

Mitter, S. (1995). Information technology and working women's demand. In S. Mitter & S. Rowbotham (Eds.), Women encounter technology: Changing patterns of employment in the Third World (pp. 19-43). New York: Routledge.

Momsen, J. H. (1991). Women and development in the Third World. New York: Routledge.

Same (1998). Gender bias in development. In A. Gonzalez & J. Norwine (Eds.), The new Third World (pp. 93-111). Boulder, CO: Westview Press.

Nelson, N. (1981). Mobilizing village women: Some organizational and management considerations. The Journal of Development Studies, 17(3), 47-58.

Nzewi, U. (1996). Involving women in science, technology, and mathematics (STM): Obstacles, remedies and challenges for national development. Paper presented at the 8th International Conference of the Gender and Science and Technology Association (GASAT), Ahmedabad, India.

Overholt, C., Anderson, M. B., Cloud, K, & Austin, J. (1985). Women in development: A framework for project analysis. In C. Overholt, M. B. Anderson, K. Cloud, & J. E. Austin (Eds.), Gender roles in development projects (pp. 3-15). West Hartford, CT: Kumarian Press.

Pena, D. G. (1997). The terror of the machine: Technology, work, gender, & ecology on the U. S.- Mexican border. Austin, TX: CMAS Books.

Quisumbing, A. R. (1998). Women in agricultural systems. In N. P. Stromquist (Ed.), Women in the Third World: An encyclopedia of contemporary issues (pp. 261-272). New York: Garland.

Quisumbing, A. R., Brown, L. R., Feldstein, H. S., Haddad, L., & Pena, C. (1995). Women: The key to food security. Washington, DC: The International Food Policy Research Institute.

Rengel, M. (2000, August 21). Women trailing in high-tech excitement. St. Cloud Times, p. 6A.

Roy, D. K. S. (1995). Women, new technology and development. New Delhi, India: Manohar.

Soliman, A. (Executive Producer). (1993, June 13). CNN world report. Atlanta, GA and Washington, DC: Cable Network News

Srinivasan, M. (1981). Impact of selected industrial technologies on women in Mexico. In R. Dauber & M. L. Cain (Eds.), Women and technological change in developing countries (pp. 89-108). Boulder, CO: Westview Press.

Summers, L. (1992, August). The most influential investment. Scientific American, p. 132.

Tadesse, Z. (1982). Women and technology in peripheral countries: An overview. In P. M. D'Onofrio-Flores & S. M. Pfafflin (Eds.), Scientific-technological change and the role of women in development (pp. 77-111). Boulder, CO: Westview Press.

Tinker, I. (1981). New technologies for food-related activities: An equity strategy. In R. Dauber & M. L. Cain (Eds.), Women and technological change in developing countries (pp. 51-88). Boulder, CO: Westview Press.

Topouzis, D. (1990, July-August). The feminization of poverty. Africa Report, pp. 60-63.

United Nations International Children Emergency Fund (1994). The progress of nations. New York: UNICEF House.

United Nations Development Program (1995). Human development report, 1995. New York: Oxford University Press.

United Nations Development Program (1997). Human development report, 1997. New York: Oxford University Press.

UNIFEM – United Nations Development Fund for Women: Working for women's economic and political empowerment. (1998). WIN News, 24(3), 3.

World Bank. (2000). World development report. New York: Oxford University Press.

World Bank (2001). World development report. New York: Oxford University Press.

Young, K. (1993). Planning development with women: Making a world of difference. New York: St. Martin's Press.